SIGNALS IN THE ANIMAL WORLD

By

DIETRICH BURKHARDT

WOLFGANG SCHLEIDT

HELMUT ALTNER

with the collaboration of

HELMUT ALBRECHT   KARL DAUMER

IRENÄUS EIBL-EIBESFELDT   KLAUS HOFFMANN

WERNER JACOBS   ARTHUR A. MYRBERG JUN.   MAXIMILIAN RENNER

FRIEDRICH SCHALLER   HERMANN SCHÖNE   JOHANN SCHWARTZKOPFF

GERNOT WENDLER   WOLFGANG WICKLER

Translated by Kenneth Morgan

McGraw-Hill Book Company

New York   Toronto   London   Sydney

Translated from the German
SIGNALE IN DER TIERWELT
© Heinz Moos Verlagsgesellschaft, 1966.

This translation © George Allen & Unwin, Ltd., 1967

Library of Congress Catalog Card Number: 67-29195
09050

Printed in West-Germany

FOREWORD

Man has always been interested in the behaviour of animals and zoologists have long been endeavouring to explain why an animal behaves in one particular way and no other in a certain situation. Now in the last few decades answers to these problems have been found. The reason is, perhaps, that all these questions are being dealt with together, systematically and with new methods in a rapidly developing branch of zoology – the study of behaviour. A further reason for this progress is that zoologists and communications engineers have realized that they are often tackling questions which are very similar in themselves or in the way they are formulated. The mutual stimulation existing among specialized fields of study, which first began as a disconnected and haphazard affair, has proved extraordinarily fruitful. Finally, another reason is that modern physics and modern electronic engineering have developed new and highly successful procedures which the zoologist can use to investigate animal activity.

If one wants to find out why an animal behaves in a particular way under certain conditions the actual working of the animal body must first be understood. What does the eye do and how is the image of the surrounding world transmitted to the brain? All these questions can be grouped together under the heading: Elements of Data Processing in the Organism. The next step is to examine how the animal behaves in its environment, how it finds its way about the world, how it recognizes food, predators and members of the species. In this case it is not the elementary part of the organism which is the subject of inquiry but a system in which the animal as a whole is only a part. And so we have a second heading: Interaction between the Animal and its Environment. An especially important part of an animal's environment is made up of the other members of the species. How does an animal communicate (in either a friendly or inimical sense) with its fellow members? Thus this aspect of the relationship between the animal and its environment falls naturally under a third heading: Animal Language. If one draws a parallel with communication techniques, analogies with all these themes are found to exist. The aim of the communications engineer is to develop the best and most efficient structural parts. He must analyse the mutual interaction of the separate components within a larger system to be able to build efficient automata. Finally, he is interested in the problem of 'language', i.e. of communication. These common interests explain why the mutual stimulation between these two spheres of work has of late been so fruitful. The fact that the questions confronting them have a common feature should not, however, lead us into confusing the objectives of biology and technology, which are different. Utopian statements and uncritical minds have already given rise to considerable misunderstanding. If the communications engineer has a problem to solve he is only interested in finding the best of perhaps many possible solutions. For the biologist, on the other hand, there is only one answer to his question. He must be able to describe, exactly, the solution which nature already offers him. In nature this solution, reached at some stage in the course of millions of years, has matured gradually through the evolution of the animal species. In fact, the most suitable solution is always found in organisms. 'Suitable' means, however, that something new evolved in the course of history out of what was available at the time. The engineer is allowed to jettison things which have been superseded. A living creature carries its own history and the history of its forbears within itself. This often obscures the problem which, because of its complexity, cannot be described in every case with mathematical precision. This is all the more reason for describing the solution as clearly and as detailed as possible.

This book attempts to show the position as it is today in the relatively young science of the study of behaviour–the results, the explanations, the premises from which it sets out and the methods and aids it employs. Writers who have specialized in this field were asked to contribute to the various subjects and themes. Their individual style was to be preserved. We hope the result is a general survey of the subject and that the danger that the dust of scholarship might dim the joy of learning something about the wonderful and surprising world of animals has been avoided.

The Editors.

When we try to understand animal behaviour we fall all too easily victims to prejudice. As men we are the prisoners of the achievements of our own senses, the richness of our own experience and of our consciousness. Without really being aware that we are doing so, we like to judge animals in the same way as our fellow men and the more they are like us the more we do this. It can be carried to the point where, quite unfairly, even human moral standards are applied to them.

Occasionally, however, animals do something which we do not understand because it does not fit into our human classifications. Then we rush in with an 'explanation', we speak of 'miracles', of the 'riddles of nature' and finally we classify what we do not understand as 'instinctive'.

Can we escape our own prejudices? Are we not too firmly bound to them to be able to construct an objective picture of other creatures? Is it even possible to look round at our own environment 'with the eye of a fly'? to imagine how it finds its way about in its world? to learn how it communicates with another fly? A philosopher would perhaps solve this problem by going deeply into the question as to whether flies have a consciousness. An engineer would approach the problem by building a model of a fly which functions with the greatest possible efficiency. Zoologists are more interested in the detail. They begin by investigating the fly's eyes, its brain (however small it may be), the connection paths (nerves) between these organs; they carry out research into the effective stimuli, observe the responses which are elicited and slowly, bit by bit, they gain some insight into a tiny, highly complex 'perceiving and thinking machine'. Does this expose or destroy the miracle?

Our love of surprise is probably too great for us to want to give it up. Unbounded astonishment at the riddles of nature has given way to surprise at nature's great lead over the much vaunted inventiveness of the human mind.

In any case, with the increasing complexity of processes clarity is often lost. If an animal can perceive stimuli which lie outside the limits of our own sense organs–examples which come to mind are ultra-violet or infra-red light, ultra sound and electrical fields–we can always fall back on the rather inadequate device of metaphor–rather as when we describe bats' ultrasonic echo location as 'image-hearing'.

If one intends to study the achievements of animals' senses, the way animals find their way about their environment and how they understand one another, then it is necessary to state a few basic facts and underlying premises.

Like all scientists, zoologists have developed a technical language in which the words bear a precise, fixed meaning, allowing facts to be described briefly and with a minimum of misunderstanding. Let us look more closely at the following three important concepts: sense organ, stimulus and excitation.

The sense organs are the instruments which an animal uses for measuring. Like scientific instruments, they measure certain physical or chemical conditions and the changes which these undergo. These conditions may exist outside the body, for instance light, external temperature or odour; but there may also be conditions existing inside the body itself, such as body temperature, blood pressure or the oxygen content of the blood. Scientific measuring instruments are so constructed as to give a maximum response to one particular physical state while remaining unaffected by others. A lightmeter is intended for measuring light and the reading must not be influenced by temperature. It is exactly the same with the sense organs: they, too, are selectively sensitive to a specific state. The physical or chemical condition to which the sense organ responds with especial sensitivity is called the 'adequate stimulus'.

How sensitive can sense organs be? Energy is required for an instrument pointer to give a reading. Even if an amplifier is incorporated to provide the necessary energy, some energy is still needed to make the amplifier work. Hence it must follow that only such physical or chemical states–or the changes which they undergo–can act as stimuli which supply energy to the sense organ. It is almost impossible to imagine how minute this amount of energy is in a highly sensitive sense organ. About 10^{-18} Watt seconds*–the one thousand millionth part of a thousand millionth part of a Watt second–is sufficient to affect the human eye or ear. And many sense organs in animals are equally sensitive. The chemical energy of a few molecules of an odorous substance is enough for butterflies to perceive scent. Underground vibrations which deliver to the sense organ an energy in the magnitude of 10^{-18} Watt seconds can be perceived by an insect. Let us now look at the tremendous number of different things that the senses can do. Everyone knows that there are animals which can see better in the dark than we do and animals which can hear better and smell better. Their sense organs, which are similar to ours, are more sensitive. But not only can certain sense organs be more–or less–sensitive than ours, their effective operating range can be different. For our eyes light with a wave-length of 400–750 nanometres** (nm) is adequate stimulus. Insects, however, perceive light with wave-lengths of 300–650 nm and can, therefore, see ultra-violet light but not light which to us looks red. Sound of over 20 kilocycles per second is inaudible to us, but bats, rodents, many carnivores, and insects hear well into the ultrasonic range. Animals have still more surprises for us. While our eye resolves the space-time organization of our environment according to the intensity and wave-length of light (corresponding to our sensations of brightness and colour), many invertebrates can recognize the direction of polarized light. We are quite unable to imagine how such a world can look. The importance of this ability was first demonstrated in 1950 by Karl von Frisch in a series of brilliant experiments. If bees are unable to see the sun but can see just a patch of blue sky they are still able to orientate themselves with respect to the sun, for the polarization pattern of the light from the blue sky bears a known relationship to the sun's position, in accordance with a scientific law. If the polarization is artificially altered by the use of polarization foils the bees fly away exactly as one would expect. The sense organs of some fishes can also do something which ours cannot: they can perceive electrical fields.

Here is a short list which will give a general idea of the physical and chemical data and conditions which can be registered by sense organs.

* 1 kilowatt hour = 3,600,000 Watt seconds
** 1 nanometre (nm) = 10^{-9}m, i.e. one thousand millionth of a metre

Mechanical senses:	Contact with the body surfaces
	Flow of a medium round the body
	Sound in air and water, underground vibration
	Position, tension and length of parts of the body
	Blood pressure
	Linear acceleration, rotational movements and rotational acceleration of the body
Light senses:	Ultra-violet to red wave-lengths
	Resolution of intensity
	Composition of wave-length
	Polarization of light
Temperature senses:	Sense organs which respond to temperature, mostly two types, one responding in particular to 'cold' the other to 'warm'
	Sense organs for radiant heat (infra-red)
Chemical senses:	Odorous substances dissolved in water or air.
	Taste substances, divided into the categories of sweet, sour, salty, bitter
	Sense organs responsive to CO_2, to the humidity of the air, to osmotic pressure, and to pH (acidity)
Electrical senses:	Sense organs which measure current density in the neighbourhood of the surfaces of the body

The above list is in no way comprehensive or detailed; but it does give some idea of the vast number of things that can be detected by organisms. The existence of sense organs which react to magnetic fields, radio waves, X-rays and to radioactivity has not yet been proved, but there is no lack of indications or speculation about these possibilities.

Of the three concepts–sense organs, stimulus and excitation–the last has so far not been mentioned. To explain it let us again borrow from the language of technology. Here the following construction principle has recently been successfully employed. With the use of suitable transducers, non-electrical quantities are converted into electrical quantities (current, voltage, resistance), which are then measured. For example, the mercury thermometer is replaced by a resistance thermometer which measures the flow of current which changes with a change of temperature. Such a method is convenient because the electrical current produced can immediately be applied to work the electrical apparatus which, in turn, controls other operations: from the thermostat on the wall a lead goes to the oil burner in the cellar, where electrically operated valves determine the supply of oil. Organisms anticipated this principle millions of years ago. The sense organs transform the various quantities into something uniform, which is called excitation. This excitation travels along nerve fibres to the central nervous system, and from there to the effector organs–muscles, glands, luminous organs, electric organs, pigment cells etc. What is this excitation which travels along nerves and is integrated by nerve cells? According to our present knowledge it is an electro-chemical process which takes place at the surface of the cell and which can propagate itself independently and with undiminished strength along a great number of cells. The process can move directly from cell to cell by electrical currents or by means of special chemical compounds (transmitters). The contact points between the cells of sense organs, between nerve cells and the cells of effector organs are called synapses. Sensory cells are, therefore, cells which not only measure certain conditions but reproduce the quantities in their excitation and pass it on to nerve cells. These again are specialized for conduction and evaluation. A characteristic feature of effector organs is that their specific activity–such as the contraction of a muscle–is governed by nerve excitation. A second principle allowing parts of the organism to be influenced by other organs is, however, also available. Messenger substances, or hormones, are produced in certain places, distributed through the body fluids and thus reach the responsive organs. Both systems work in close collaboration and dovetail into one another. Nerve cells can produce hormones and nerve cells can respond very sensitively to hormones.

All this might give the impression that the zoologist's work consisted solely of dissecting the organism into little pieces and investigating their individual function. But this is only part of his job. A further, important step is to examine the interaction among these parts. All the time countless messages flow in to the central nervous system from the sense organs. Not all of them are absolutely essential at the time. The nervous system must therefore filter out what is important. Further, the messages from different sense organs and stored data are brought into relationship with one another in the central nervous system. This involves two factors: data and knowledge (memory) acquired in the course of the individual life and also innate knowledge which is passed on from generation to generation. Bees can be trained to recognize time, place and scent: that is, they learn. On the other hand they have an innate understanding of the signals which fellow members of the hive make in the bee dance and they can orientate themselves innately by the sun. But it is not only data from the sense organs and data stored in the central nervous system which are evaluated before a definite action is performed. Animals are prepared to do certain actions at certain times, but not at others. A 'clockwork' ensures that actions are performed periodically or even just once, at a definite time. What this internal clock is and how it functions is a focal point of interest at the moment. Hormone control probably plays an important part in this. At this stage of the analysis an attempt to discover basic principles will also be made. How do the separate parts work together? An essential process in the organism is that of autonomous control, by means of self-regulating control circuits. Sense organs, like instruments, show deviations from some desired state, for instance from the usual position in space. After consideration in the central nervous system this message is sent to organs which make the necessary correction, i. e. corresponding limb movements which restore the desired position. In this way relatively simple connections guarantee that certain conditions in the organism will remain constant.

Generally speaking the simplest of behaviour patterns will accomplish what appear to be very complicated things. Examples of this appear in the direction of animals' movement in response to stimuli. An animal always turns its back to the light. As the centre of gravity of light is normally in the middle of the sky, it flies or swims horizontally. If an animal always tries to get away from the earth–negative geotaxis, to use the zoologist's technical term–it is certain to finish up at that part of a plant where it will find food: the greenfly will get to the juicy tip of a young shoot and the ant gets to the greenfly which it can milk.

When an animal orientates itself in its environment several senses often work in conjunction with one another. It is not only important to know what sort of odorous substance is in the air, but also where it comes from. Olfactory sense organs give the alert, sense organs able to detect air currents provide information about the direction. Depending on the significance of the odour the animal faces into the wind, then moves forward and finds what it wants or it turns away and flees from the evil. The analytical method allows behaviour patterns to be deciphered. Movement is separated from orientation, the adjustment of direction in respect of a source of stimulation. The latter component is called 'taxis'. Positive taxis is orientation movement towards a stimulus; negative taxis is movement away from a stimulus; menotaxis is maintenance of a definite angle to a stimulus–for example, when a course is set and kept by using the sun as a compass.

An animal's habits largely determine which of its organs are important for orientation. A fish living on the muddy bed of standing water will have little use for highly developed eyes. Barbels are of more value to it as organs of feeling and taste. A trout living in a clear mountain stream can remain stationary on one spot if it swims face on to the current with the help of its lateral line system and by using its eyes keeps close to the markings on the bank. A very simple experiment proves that fish do this: A fish is put into an artificial circular stream in the middle of which there is a metal cylinder on which stripes have been painted. It takes up a position head on to the current and remains in the same place. If the cylinder is carefully rotated the fish swims round in a circle, following the revolving cylinder.

After the second part of the book has shown some of the methods which animals use to orientate themselves in their environment, the third part goes into the question of how animals communicate and understand one another.

What do we understand by an 'animal language'? Were we not repeatedly assured that one of the cardinal differences between animals and men was that only the latter had developed a language? Now a language which is made up of sentences containing a subject and a predicate has not been found among animals. But the signals which animals make, their calls, their movements and the positions they adopt can, despite the absence of a grammar, express something definitely factual, such as: "Come here!", "Clear off!", "Get out of my territory!", "Build a nest with me", "Help! I'm lost", or even "Fly straight on keeping about 30 degrees left of the sun and then, about 200 yards away, you will find a mass of clover in flower." This last piece of information could come from a bee which has just discovered a rich source of food and is telling the other bees in the hive. Karl von Frisch, who has deciphered this signal language, coined the phrase 'Language of the Bees'. How else should we describe this sort of exchange of information?

Signals between members of the same species and even between creatures of different species are as common as life itself. Even the individual egg cell sends out chemical signals and attracts spermatozoa. The pollen grains of flowering plants orientate themselves in a chemical field when they have reached the stigma of a blossom and send the pollen ampula to the egg cell in the ovary. The fact of 'sexuality', the fact that there are two sexes which must meet in order to produce offspring makes it necessary for members of the species to attract members of the opposite sex, or at least to inform them of one's own sex. Just as important as attracting the sexual partner is the need, in many cases, to keep other members of the species (as one's most dangerous rivals) at a distance and from access to one's food. Here, we may say, is the origin of 'aggression' and combat produces further signals–challenging, intimidating, expressing inferiority and the like. On the other hand many animals find that it pays to band themselves together into groups, perhaps to exploit food sources more efficiently (for instance by hunting prey in packs) or to defend themselves more effectively against enemies. This makes it essential to be able to report the exact location of food sources (as in the above example of the bees), to arrange a raid or to warn the group of an approaching enemy. And if a member of the group gets lost it is, in many cases, guided back by the calls of its fellows to the safety of the community.

But how do animals come to understand what the individual signals mean? Must they, like us, learn the meaning of individual 'words', or is it a question of inborn ability? Now, we know examples of both of these and also various intermediate forms; e.g. an animal can utter a certain call or pose a certain signal position in a certain situation innately, but it has to learn the significance of a member of the species making the same call or showing the same signal position. From the way the signal is made or from the response which is released it is possible to deduce with a reasonable degree of probability *how* understanding between sender and receiver has been achieved. And so it can be stated, as a general rule, that the animal must learn complicated signals but that it has an innate understanding for the simpler ones. Recognizing calls which are composed of a long, changing sequence of tones or of optical 'sign stimuli' whose effectiveness depends on all the component features being visible *and* arranged coherently in a definite situation (the so-called 'Gestalten' of Gestalt psychology) must be learned. Short calls, often monotonously repeated, or optical sign stimuli which are just simple colours, simple movements or which contrast with the background are, in the main, understood innately. Another general rule is that the mechanisms which produce signals can be less influenced by experience than the mechanisms which recognize signals: in other words, signals are more often made innately than they are understood.

In the last paragraph the expression 'sign stimulus' was used. While the term 'stimulus' is used just for simple physical states or changes of state, in the study of behaviour 'sign stimulus' is used for both stimuli and also combinations of stimuli which release, maintain or inhibit behaviour patterns. But a sign stimulus need not necessarily be a signal as well, if the latter is understood as a sort of message and as a help to understanding. An animal which is in danger of being discovered and eaten by an enemy does its best not to betray its presence. Nevertheless sign stimuli go out from it which, if they reach an enemy, release the latter's predatory behaviour response. One and the same sign stimulus can, of course, be both a signal for another member of the species and also a help to the predator in finding its prey. Mice and shrews communicate and understand one another by using high pitched tones which lie in the ultrasonic range. Many predators which live primarily on mice, such as cats, foxes and probably also the ancestors of the domestic dog, are much larger than their prey and achieve understanding with their own kind by means of deeper sounds; but they find it an advantage to listen to the conversation of their prey. This explains why predators specializing in mice have developed especially acute hearing and are far superior to us and even to many other animals of the same size in sensitivity to high pitched tones in the upper range of hearing.

Movements and organs which were developed in the course of the history of the species for sending out sign stimuli in the service of communication are called 'releasers'. Such releasers–they could also be called 'emitting apparatus for key stimuli'–naturally did not come into existence overnight, but have evolved in the course of thousands or millions of years. They arose out of movements which originally had nothing to do with signalling, but were connected with cleaning, nest building, locomotion, breathing (vocalization, song) and involve a variety of organs. One has only to think of the pinna which, created in the first place to improve the directional sensitivity of the organ of hearing, can, as a releaser, express a mood; or of the tail of vertebrates which originally was used exclusively to give forward propulsion–as it is used by fish even today–and came later to be used purely as a rudder (in birds and mammals) and also as the carrier of an amazing variety of releasers of social behaviour. The same applies to all kinds of skin covering (scales, feathers and hair) which serve primarily to protect and to insulate, and are also the bearers of every imaginable kind of releaser. Konrad Lorenz writes: "Releasers are uncommonly widespread in the case of birds. It is scarcely an exaggeration to say that all very 'conspicuous' colours and plumage are connected with releasing functions." Corresponding to the releaser, in its role as an emitting apparatus, there is in the receiver a more or less selectively tuned receiving apparatus for sign stimuli which we describe as a 'releasing mechanism'. Releasing mechanisms are filter-like structures of a sense organ and (or) parts of the nervous system, especially the brain, connected with them. The tuning to a sign stimulus is frequently done in accordance with the principle of the band-pass filter: the releaser, for example, would be the yellow marking on a cichlid when she is tending the brood. The sign stimulus (yellow) makes the young fish follow it. With inexperienced young fish a yellow coloured fish dummy produces the same effect; a green or orange dummy is less effective, while blue or red dummies are hardly noticed. The 'innate releasing mechanism' of the following response is in this case selectively tuned to the mother's yellow breeding dress. In other cases the selectivity is based on a principle which is best compared with a high-pass filter. An example of this is the mechanism which releases the courting response in a male fritillary. The dummies representing a female are just as effective as the living prototype if the wings beat at the same rate. If the dummy wings beat more slowly it is less effective; but if it beats faster it is preferred to the genuine female. In fact, the faster the wings beat the more it is preferred. This method of tuning a releasing mechanism is not so fine but it makes it possible for the releaser to advance into a higher, more favourable range and allows room for 'improvement'. For the signals which animals send out are not fixed once and for all but naturally have the same opportunity as every other 'organ' for further evolution.

How the Eye Controls an Insect's Movement

For bees, flies, dragonflies, butterflies and many other insects the eye is a most important sense organ. It controls their quick, skillful manoeuvres. It measures, regulates and directs the course and speed of their flight above the ground and the turning of their body. At the same time it acts as a compass. It enables the insect to maintain a course independently of landmarks simply by using the position of the sun and the resulting pattern of polarized light in the blue sky. The colour vision of bees, for instance, is quite different from ours, but is probably just as highly developed. Bees cannot see red; but they can see ultra-violet. They can single out the richest sources of food from among a mass of brilliant flowers and recognize them again by their colour. The importance of the eye for insects becomes obvious when one considers what a large portion of the brain is available to integrate the messages coming from the eye. In flies this is a full two thirds of the entire brain.

An insect's eye is quite different in structure from a human eye. As an example let us take the eye of the bluebottle (*Calliphora erythrocephala*). This has some 40,000 visual cells, whereas the human eye has 100 million. Every seven cells (in other insects the number may differ between six and eight) are arranged in a single group. Each group is like a slender cone and is completely encased with a screen of pigment cells. These prevent disturbing side light from reaching the visual cells. Each group of visual cells receives light only through its individual lens system. The lenses of the groups of visual cells can be seen as tiny facets on the surface of the whole eye, hence the name compound eye. Each group of visual cells with its outer sheath of pigment cells and its system of lenses is called an ommatidium. Many thousands of these cone-shaped ommatidia–in flies the number is 5½ thousand–are packed close together like the quills of a hedgehog which has rolled up into a ball. Figs. 1 and 2 illustrate this. Each individual cell detects the brightness, colour (wavelength) and polarization of the light within a small angle of the surroundings. The eight visual cells of an ommatidium are quite distinct in character. Each one is orientated in a particular direction to catch the polarized light and some are specially tuned to certain other wavelengths. The extent to which the various visual cells in the

Figure 2. Diagram of three groups of visual cells. Each group has its own dioptric apparatus, consisting of a lens (L) and a further structure of high refractive power, the crystalline cone (C). Principal and secondary pigment cells (P and S) screen the groups from oblique rays of light. The inner parts of the visual cells (V) are called rhabdomes (Rh). A slightly enlarged cross-section of a group can be seen on the right.

group are stimulated depends on the colour of the object which the lens forms in the ommatidium. Again, the degree to which other visual cells in the group are affected depends on the orientation of the plane of polarized light from the sky.

There are several hundreds of thousands of nerve cells behind the eye, available to act as an apparatus for evaluating this pattern. In a minute fraction of a second the shape and colour of an object are classified from the messages appearing on the screen of the visual cells, the polarized light patterns which the human eye never sees are interpreted and finally the velocity and direction of an image moving over the whole eye are calculated. Changing images of this kind appear if an object near the fly moves or if the fly itself moves.

The creature not only assimilates all this optical data in less than a tenth of a second, it also begins to react. Anyone who has ever tried to catch a fly with his hand is well aware of this. It soon becomes obvious that the fly's eye is anything but slow. For us 20 or more flashes of light in a second merge to make a continuous impression of light; for flies, however, there have to be more than 200 flashes a second for the same thing to happen. In other words, a fly's power to resolve patterns in time with its eye is much greater than ours. Therefore, because of their speedier reaction, the fly's smaller number of visual cells can tell it almost as much about its surroundings as the human eye's vastly greater number of

Figure 1. Head of a gad-fly (Tabanus bromius). The two big eyes, fixed rigidly in the head, can survey almost the whole of the area around the insect.

visual cells. The optic nerve centres connected to a fly's eye are like an incredibly efficient computer. What is more, these cells occupy less space than a single transistor, the smallest component in a modern electronic computer. Fig. 3 gives some idea of the connections in an optical nerve centre in a fly's brain. Nerve fibres criss-cross one another, make contact in innumerable places and thus integrate the stream of information coming from the eye.

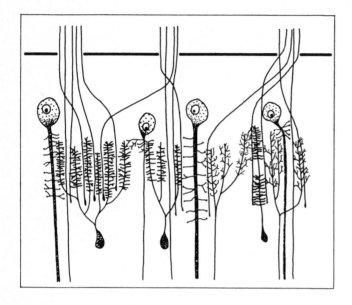

Figure 3. Diagram of a few types of nerve cells and nerve fibres in the optical centre in the brain of a fly immediately next to the eye. The nerve processes extending from the visual cells (to be imagined above the drawing) are here for the most part in contact with more nerve fibres. Thus criss-crossings and cross-connections behind the eye allow interpretation of the individual messages coming from the visual cell array. The contacts of the nerve cells with one another occur at the brush-like ramifications. Only a few types of the vast number of nerve cells are shown and of these only very few have been drawn.

Colour Photograph. Close-up picture of the eye of a gad-fly (Tabanus bromius). The large compound eyes take up two thirds of the face of a gad-fly. Lenses are in regular hexagonal arrays. Deep behind there are light-sensitive cells for each lens. The macrophotograph shows only a small section of the insect's eye (magnified about 300 times). The rainbow pattern on the surface of the eye is made by the iridescent colours produced by interference on thin layers. Figure 1 gives the general picture.

Light-Eyes and Radiant Heat-Eyes

The communications engineer can use two different methods to demonstrate the existence of electro-magnetic waves. In the first a receiver is tuned so that it is selectively stimulated by the vibration frequency concerned. After adequate amplification by electronic valves or transistors, this vibration is fed to a suitable recording apparatus. In the second method the electro-magnetic wave is absorbed, the energy being converted into heat which can be shown by a sensitive thermometer.

In the animal world only a very narrow band of the entire electro-magnetic range is employed to receive signals from the environment or to transmit signals. These are the frequencies of a magnitude of 10^{14} cycles per second, which we call light. Eyes and other organs sensitive to light but of less highly developed structure are receivers. The luminous organs possessed by many animal species are emitters. There is also a second, narrower band, with frequencies of a magnitude of 10^{13} cycles per second, called infra-red or radiant heat. Here the receivers are sense organs which respond to temperature. In this case nature clearly works in accordance with the second of these two principles mentioned above, while in the reception of visible light the principle of selective tuning operates. In animal eyes there are always visual cells, highly specialized sensory cells and also various kinds of auxiliary cells. Parts of the visual cells contain molecules of a certain type of chemical compound, a visual pigment. Investigation of this pigment in a test tube shows that it does not absorb light of all wave-lengths to the same extent, but only light from specific wave bands. The tuning of the pigment to definite wave-lengths is not very sharp. A deviation of 10% from the most favourable wave-length cuts the absorption of energy to about half the maximum. The absorption maximum of the known pigments lies mainly in the band between 500–550 nm, that is at frequencies of about 5.10^{14} cycles per second. (1 nm = 1 nanometre = 10^{-9} = one thousand millionth part of a metre.) In addition to a primary maximum in this wave band, many pigments have a secondary maximum at 360 nm that is, in the ultra-violet band. This secondary maximum has no effect on our eyes. As the lens and the vitreous body of the eye absorb ultra-violet, it does not reach the visual cells. Light of 540 nm is therefore the brightest colour of the spectrum—a yellowish green. The secondary maximum at 360 nm has, however, a definite effect on insects' eyes. Insects can see ultra-violet. Many animals can distinguish colours, that is, light stimuli composed of different wave-lengths appear to them not only of varying degrees of brightness but also of different quality for the same amount of energy. This can be explained if one assumes that their eyes contain several pigments tuned to different wave-lengths. The impulse pattern in the optic nerve then depends not only on the spatial and temporal distribution of the light stimuli on the retina, but also on the wave-length. Since the work of Young and of Helmholtz it has been assumed that there must be three such receptors for different wave-lengths. A few years ago the first successful investigation of the individual visual cells of flies was carried out. Most of them showed an absorption maximum at 490 nm but a few did so at 470 nm and a few at 520 nm with all the visual cells showing a secondary maximum at 360 nm. Studies of the visual cells of bees, whose colour vision cannot be doubted, soon followed. In their case, too, there were at least three different types of visual cells, with an absorption maximum at 360 nm, at 430 nm and 470 nm, and finally at 540 nm. Very recently it also became possible, by using different methods, to investigate the visual cells of mammals and of human beings. Once again three kinds of visual cells were found, this time with absorption maxima at 430, 540 and 575 nm respectively.

All these experiments show that colour vision occurs throughout the animal kingdom because at least three different types of visual cells in eyes able to see colour are tuned to different wave-lengths. Finally it should be mentioned that biochemical research has also shown that there is an astonishing uniformity within the animal kingdom. All visual pigments so far analyzed belong to the same group of chemical compounds, being derivatives of vitamin A and bound to a protein. Relatively small modifications of the chemical structure of these pigments make it possible for the absorption maximum to be tuned to different wave-lengths. In spite of this possibility of variation, the area in which this principle functions seems to be extremely restricted. The sensitivity of all eyes so far investigated does not exceed wave-lenghts of 300 or 800 nm and therefore remains between frequencies of 4.10^{14} and 10^{15} cycles per second. Receptors for shorter wave-lengths have not yet been discovered. On the other hand there are receptors for longer wave-lengths, infra-red or radiant heat, but they work on an entirely different principle. We ourselves can roughly locate radiant heat, say from an electric fire. The warming of the body surface by the rays is felt by temperature organs in the skin. Compared with the eye they can locate objects

Figure 1. Head of a rattle-snake (Crotalus viridis) with the pit organs which lie below the line joining the nostril and the eye.

only very inaccurately. Moreover, they are very insensitive. Many million times more radiant heat is required for the perception of a source of radiant heat than for the perception of a source of light. There is, however, one sub-order of living creatures in which this way of receiving radiant energy has developed to such a pitch of perfection that one is inclined to speak of infra-red eyes. These are the snakes, of which two families possess efficient sense organs of this kind–large snakes of the *Pytonidae* family and rattle-snakes, *Crotalidae*. Between the nostril and the eye on both sides of a rattle-snake's head there is a pit which is partly covered by a thin membrane. These membranes readily absorb radiant heat of wave-lengths between 1.5 and 15 nm, that is, frequencies of 10^{13} cycles per second. As the membrane is horny, very thin–about $\frac{15}{1000}$ mm–and covers an air-filled space immediately behind it (Fig. 2), its heat capacity is small and it is noticeably warmed by radiant heat. The radiant heat of a mouse 15 cm away from the head of a snake produces a rise of about $\frac{3}{1000}$° Centigrade. The membrane is densely packed with multi-branching nerve endings which respond to every rise in temperature by sending out many more impulses. The threshold for this is below $\frac{5}{1000}$° Centigrade, that is, just low enough to detect a mouse 15 cm away. These organs are the most sensitive temperature receptors that have so far been discovered in the animal world.

As the sensory membrane is sunk slightly below the edge of the pit, heat rays from different directions fall on different parts of the membrane, all of which have different nerve

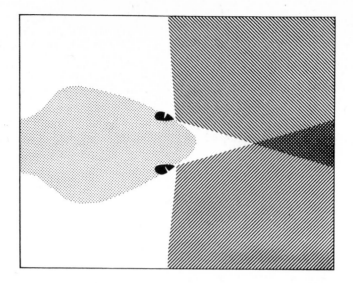

Figure 3. The two intersecting fields of view of the infra-red eyes, seen from above. While the field of view of the two organs together is more than 180°, the binocular area in front of the reptile is relatively narrow.

fibres. In this way the source of the radiant heat can be pin-pointed. Each of the two organs can perceive radiant heat within a conical field. The two cones intersect on the long axis in front of the creature's head, so that a source of heat in front of it is focussed by both infra-red eyes (Fig. 3). The reptile is thus able to pin-point warm-blooded prey–small mammals such as mice–or cold-blooded prey–such as wet frogs–against a background of a uniform temperature and also to locate and to kill them in the dark.

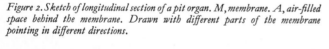

Figure 2. Sketch of longitudinal section of a pit organ. M, membrane. A, air-filled space behind the membrane. Drawn with different parts of the membrane pointing in different directions.

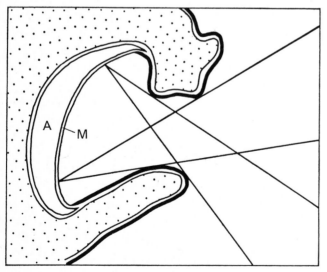

Colour Photograph. Cross-section of the eye of a fly (Calliphora erythrocephala). Magnification 2000×; azan staining technique. The parts of the visual cells which contain the pigment can be seen as blue spots in the upper half of the photograph. The sectional plane lies more deeply below the eye surface in the upper part of the photograph than in the lower part. Cf. the longitudinal section in Fig. 2, p. 19.

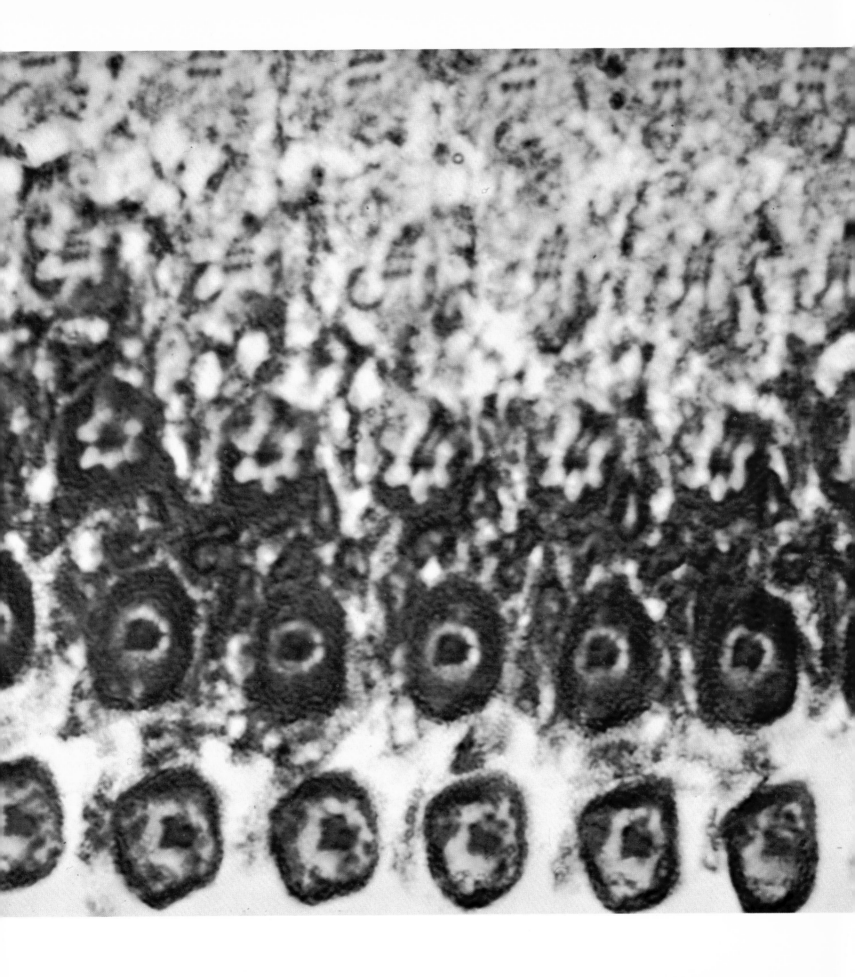

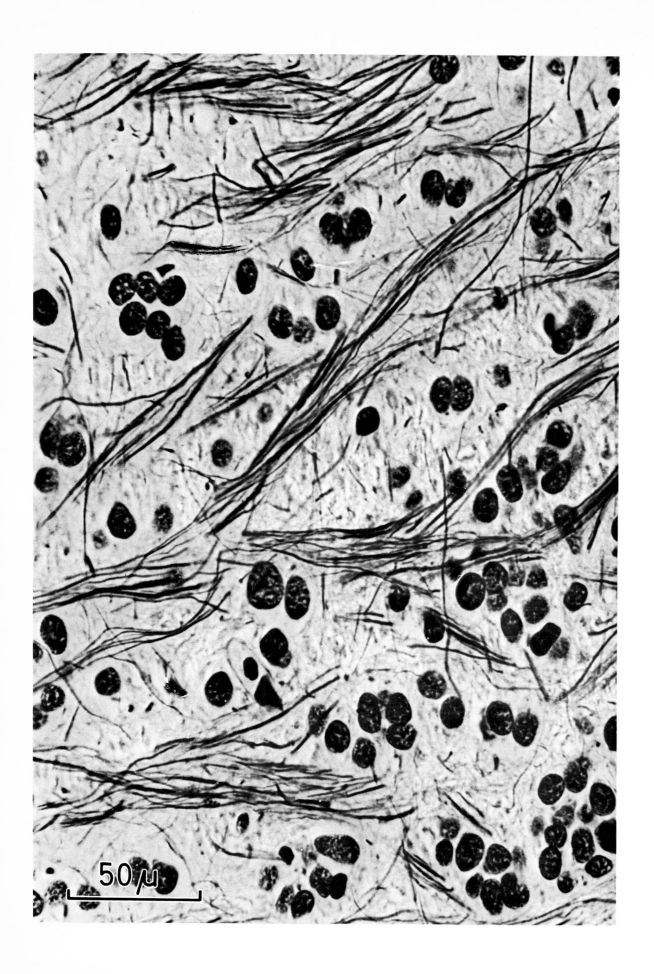
50μ

Data Processing in Vision

When we think about our ability to see, we generally think only of the importance of the eye. But most of us forget the important part which the interpretation of data in the brain plays in visual perception. Many millions of nerve cells or neurons are actively involved in this. They interpret not only messages which come from the eye but also any coming from other sense organs. The image of the external world projected on to the retina by the lens of the eye never remains still but moves constantly to and fro at every movement of the body, of the head or of the eyes. Yet the world appears to us as a stationary system of reference. A simple experiment proves that this, in fact, is not so simple as one could expect. If one shuts one eye and presses a finger into the other eye, the world tilts over in a most unpleasant fashion. And this is exactly what one would expect from the displacement of the image on the retina. If a similar displacement is produced by an eye movement, the world stays still. As the messages coming from the retina are exactly the same in both cases, other additional messages must be interpreted in the second case. In this instance we can say with great certainty that they are the orders which travel to the eye muscles to initiate the movement of the eye. They are stored for a moment in the centre. The centre expects a very definite message from the eye for this movement. Now if a message of a displaced image comes from the retina it is compared with what has been stored up and is expected. If there are no divergencies the conclusion drawn is that the world is stationary.

Other data are, however, also taken into account in these optical centres, for example any which are supplied by the labyrinth, our organ of equilibrium. If one sits down on a revolving stool and spins round the world appears to be stationary, although the image on the retina is being constantly displaced. At the same time the labyrinth sends the following message: "I am spinning round and round." This message is treated as being of the same kind but rebutting the message from the retina. This can easily be demonstrated in another way. The labyrinth is a comparatively inert organ. If the spinning stops suddenly, the labyrinth lags behind for a short while. Although the image is stationary on the retina one sees the world spinning round

because of the incorrect message sent by the labyrinth after the sudden stop. The examples given so far have all related to the way data from other sense organs are interpreted in conjunction with data from the eye. But the very act of seeing necessitates extensive calculations in the optical centres of the brain. First, a simple example to illustrate this. It is easy to demonstrate experimentally that our eye resolves colours only in the middle of our visual field. Partial colour blindness sets in towards the outer zones, and at the extreme edge the eye can discern no colours whatsoever. Yet we have the impression that our whole field of view is filled with colour. This must, therefore, be the work of central nerve cells. They either supplement correctly what is missing or they store up definite information. We constantly move our eyes, with the result that we have at some time seen the colour of the objects which shortly afterwards are on the colour-blind edge of the visual field. Fig. 1 gives some idea of the nerve connections in the optical centres of the brain. In a few favourably preserved cases details are also now known about the functioning of the nerve cells concerned in the interpretation of optical data. Nerve cells in the optical centres of the brain of prosimians are an example. Prosimians are 'eye creatures' like us; that is, the eye is the most important organ for orientation in their environment. Consequently their eyes and optical centres are especially well developed. The colour photograph shows the large eye of a prosimian, the bush-baby. In a monkey, *Macaca mulatta*, individual neurons in the optical centres were investigated while the eye was subjected to various light stimuli. In the dark most nerve cells send out nerve impulses at relatively constant intervals. If light is shone on to the eye, the frequency of the impulses increases or decreases. The frequency can, therefore, be modulated in two different directions. A more detailed investigation shows that individual nerve cells increase the frequency of their impulses quite independently of the colour of the light stimulus. The brighter the light, the greater the increase in their frequency. On the other hand, other nerve cells do not respond to the brightness of the light over wide areas but do respond to its colour or, to be more exact, to its wave-length, in a very specific way. For example, they send out more frequent impulses when red light strikes the retina. If the eye is stimulated by green light, the complementary colour, the impulses become less frequent. Another type of nerve cell does not react to red and green, but does to the complementary pair of colours blue and yellow.

As our knowledge about the activity of visual cells is now very accurate, it is possible to investigate how the central nerve cells function. One type of visual cell which reacts to a broad range of different wave-lengths affects the nerve cells in such a way that their impulses become more fre-

Figure 1. Nerve connections in the optic tectum of the black spiny dogfish (Etmopterus spinax). Silver impregnation makes the nerve fibres visible. The dark, roundish structures are cell nuclei.

quent. A second type, also sensitive to a very wide but slightly different range of spectral lights, affects the same nerve cells in such a way that their impulses become less frequent. In this way the algebraic difference is formed in the nerve cells from the messages of the various visual cells. While the activity of visual cells depends only slightly on the wave-length, this dependence has become a characteristic feature of such nerve cells. Fig. 2 shows this in a diagrammatic form. Similar experiments have also established facts about nerve cells which are concerned solely with the interpretation of movements and others which are solely concerned with the perception of shape. While these results are astonshing, it must be realized that they provide answers only to isolated problems. Much more work has to be done before we can fully understand the activity of the central nervous system.

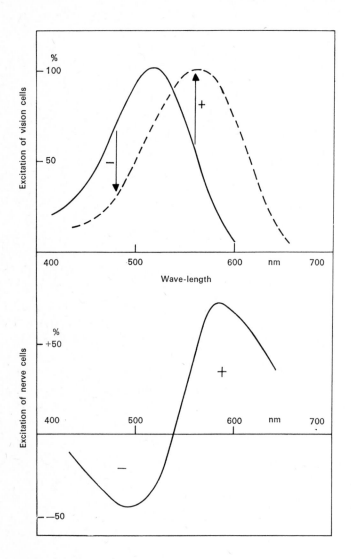

Figure 2. Diagram to illustrate the way nerve cells of the visual system evaluate colour. In the top half the activity of two different visual cells is shown to be dependent on the wavelength. Vertical axis: excitation of the visual cells on the same percentage-scale. The bottom half shows the difference of the spectral curves of the two visual cells. The difference is reflected by the frequency of the nerve cell impulses.

Colour Photograph. Young bush-baby (Galago senegalensis).

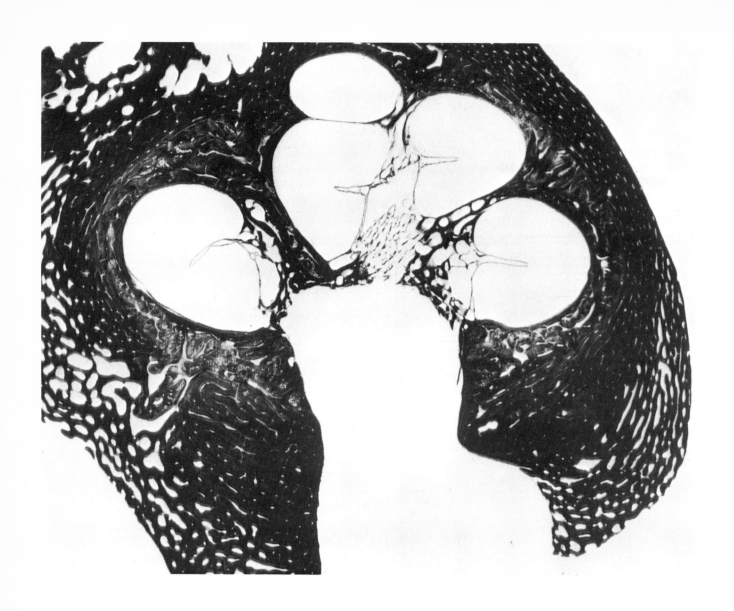

The Ear as a Signal Receiver

To the communication engineer the ear appears as a sort of information receiver. Sound vibrations bearing information about the external world strike the ear and are transformed into nerve impulses. Some of the information which was originally present gets lost in this process. The organ of hearing can deal with only part of the wide range of sound frequencies and its dynamics is limited by its own noise and by non-linear distortions. These technical data can be measured and described in the same way as a microphone or an electronic amplifier.

The ear is also like a microphone in the way it functions. It, too, transforms energy. Mechanical energy–sound vibrations–is changed into the chemical and electrical energy of nerve impulses. The place where this conversion takes place is deeply embedded in the bone called the petrosal, in the helicoid inner ear. A complicated mechanism brings the sound vibrations to it from outside (Fig. 2a). Sound-energy is funneled by the pinna and conveyed to the ear-drum via the auditory canal. The ear-drum, a thin, tightly-stretched piece of skin, vibrates at the same rate as the sound striking it and imparts its vibrations to the fluid in the inner ear by means of the ear ossicles. These ossicles ensure the correct matching between air-borne sound (on the ear-drum) and fluid-borne sound (in the inner ear). The high sound resistance at the interphase between the air and the fluid is overcome by two forms of gearing–the

levering system of the ossicles and the reduction of the area in motion. The inner ear is a coiled, spiral tube which is divided into two halves for almost its entire length by the basilar membrane (Fig. 2b, c). The inner ear is filled with fluid and has two elastically sealed 'windows' which lie against the middle ear. Fitting into the upper window like a piston in a cylinder is one of the ossicles–the stirrup–and covering the lower window is a small piece of skin which allows the fluid to give. It bulges if the stirrup presses inwards and bends the other way if the stirrup pulls outwards. The wall of the inner ear is made of bone (Fig. 1) and does not yield to the pressure. But the basilar membrane is itself set vibrating by the fluid moving to and fro in time with the stirrup. Travelling waves are set up, flowing out from the area of the windows and spreading along the basilar membrane. They immediately increase in amplitude, reach a maximum and then quickly die away. High frequency oscillations produce only a very short travelling wave and the maximum amplitude of the basilar membrane lies near the windows. The deeper a tone the further the travelling waves extend and the closer the maximum amplitude is to the apex of the cochlea. The entire length of the basilar membrane is covered with sensory cells (Fig. 2d). Those which lie within the zone of the maximum amplitude of the travelling waves are stimulated more vigorously than their neighbours and signal this message to the brain. Our subjective perception of pitch depends therefore, on which part of the basilar membrane vibrates most, and the perception of loudness depends on the absolute amplitude at the maximum vibration. The

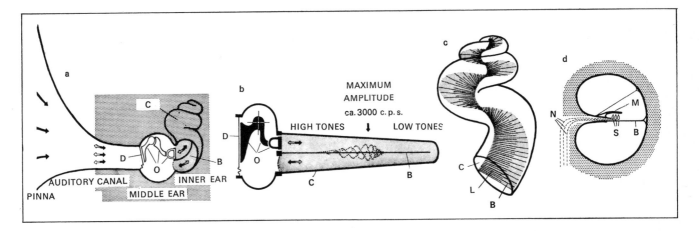

Figure 1. Axial section through the bony cochlea of a human ear, magnification about 100 ×. In this preparation all soft tissue has been destroyed, including the basilar membrane. In the cross-sections through the coils of the cochlea, however, can be seen the bony lamellae which form the inner suspension of the basilar membrane (cf. Figs. 2c and 2d). In the narrow gap between the lamellae there is room for the fibres of the auditory nerve which run from the sensory cells on the basilar membrane to the spindle of the cochlea and from there to the brain.

Figure 2a. General picture of the anatomy of the ear of a mammal. b. Simplified sketch of the principle of sound conduction from the ear-drum (D) to the cochlea (C), here shwon with the lever transmission by the ear ossicles (O) and the origin of the travelling waves of the basilar membrane (B). c. Position of the basilar membrane and the supporting lamellae (L) in the cochlea (compare with the microphotograph on the opposite page). d. Cross-section of a coil of the cochlea: tectorial membrane (M), sensory cells (S) and auditory nerve fibres (N).

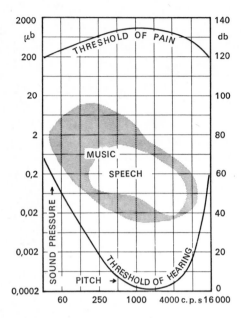

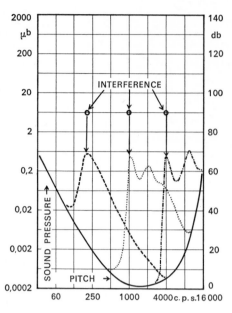

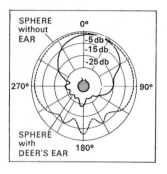

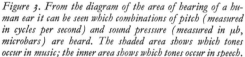

Figure 3. From the diagram of the area of hearing of a human ear it can be seen which combinations of pitch (measured in cycles per second) and sound pressure (measured in μb, microbars) are heard. The shaded area shows which tones occur in music; the inner area shows which tones occur in speech.

Figure 4. Loud tones mask a definite zone of the area of hearing below them and therefore produce a partial rise in the threshold of hearing. In a diagram of the area of hearing of the kind in Fig. 3 the areas masked by three different tones are shown.

Figure 5. Directional characteristic of the pinna of a red deer in the horizontal plane at 4,000 cycles per second. The pinna is mounted on a sphere 20 cm in diameter, the sound pressure is measured by a microphone in the auditory canal. The dotted line shows the directional characteristic of the sphere without the pinna and with the microphone set in the surface of the sphere.

louder the sound and the greater the amplitude of the vibration of the stirrup, the more the basilar membrane is moved from its resting position, the more the sensory cells are stimulated and the louder we hear the sound.

Now for the technical data about the ear. The units of measurement at the 'input' of our hearing system are, in terms of physics, clearly definable. Air-borne sound of known frequency and intensity is conveyed to the ear from a loudspeaker. But what unit is used at the 'output'? As long as it is only a matter of measuring sensitivity at different pitches of tone, the statement by the subject of the experiment is sufficient: "I hear a sound" or "I don't hear a sound." If all the measurements of the pitch of different tones at which a sound was still audible are joined up a 'threshold of hearing' curve is obtained (Fig. 3). Similarly, a 'threshold of pain' curve can be plotted by joining together the measurements of different pitches at which the sound is so intense that it causes pain. In the diagram in Fig. 3 these two curves enclose an area which is typical of the normal working range of the ear and is, for obvious reasons, called the 'area of hearing'.

This area shows, however, only the range in which hearing is *possible*, and this depends very largely on the extent to which other interfering sounds are excluded from the immediate vicinity. Fig. 4 shows three examples of how the threshold of hearing rises when interference is sent out at the same time as the reference tone. The greatest rise occurs when the reference tone and the interference are of about

the same pitch. With very loud interference, however, the next higher octave becomes involved, probably due to non-linear transmission properties in the range of the middle or inner ear.

Under normal conditions such masking effects play a significant part and they make it difficult to hear the 'biologically significant signal' among the jumble of the interference. Outer ears which have a pronounced directional characteristic can help matters considerably if the interference comes from a different direction from that of the signal. Fig. 5 shows the directional characteristic of the ear of a deer. Under favourable conditions–if, for instance, the angle between the direction of the signal and the interference is about 90°–the difference between signal and interference improves by 20–30 decibels.

Colour Photograph. Fallow deer (doe) with fawn. Both pairs of ears are pointed towards the observer. To rouse the animals' attention the photographer had clicked his tongue before taking the photograph.

Owls - Acoustic Location

Besides the eye, the ear provides us with the most important information from our environment. It is also especially important as a receiver for verbal understanding. As well as receiving sound we, like animals, can also use the ear to recognize and locate a source of sound. Nocturnal birds of prey, such as the tawny owl shown in the colour photograph and the barn owl in Fig. 1, locate their victims mainly in this way. The accuracy with which this is done–to within about 1°–is probably greater than a human being could possibly achieve. And there is a further difference. We can really only locate an object two-dimensionally, in the horizontal plane. It takes us some time to track down an aeroplane in the sky. This would probably be a very simple problem for an owl sweeping through the air since it can locate objects three-dimensionally–something absolutely essential if it is to find its prey in time.

What in particular makes it possible to hear where sound comes from? In hearing the direction of a sound a number of very different principles are involved. Only the two most important ones will be discussed here. First, each ear has its own directional characteristic. But for this similar sound waves, depending on the direction from which they arrive, would be perceived differently by one ear, some sounding louder than others (Fig. 2). This directional characteristic is determined by the structure of the outer ear, which consists of the pinna, the outer auditory canal and the ear-drum. The pinna is not always as important as one might first imagine. Nevertheless many large-eared animals can move the pinna and so locate sound much better. In many owls parts of the outer ear on both sides of the head are of slightly different shape. It has, therefore, long been assumed that their two ears have different directional fields and that this plays an important part in locating sound three-dimensionally. Finally, it must not be forgotten that the directional characteristic of the ear depends on the pitch of the sound. It becomes narrower when dealing with high frequencies. Since most sounds in our environment are made up from a wide spectrum of different frequencies, the two ears hear the same sound as having a different timbre. Depending on the direction from which the sound comes more high frequencies are filtered out by one ear than by the other. Only if both ears are directed in exactly the same way to the source of the sound is the timbre exactly the same for both.

This is what makes it possible to locate sound. For human beings, however, the location of the source of a sound with the ear's directional field is nothing like as important as the second mechanism. For us, as well as most mammals and large birds such as owls this second and particularly important principle is directional hearing by the perception of time differences. If the sound does not come from exactly in front or exactly behind, the two ears are at different distances from the source of the sound. Any sudden new sound, therefore, reaches the further ear a little later. As the speed of sound is 1,120 feet per second and the maximum difference in distance cannot be greater than the width

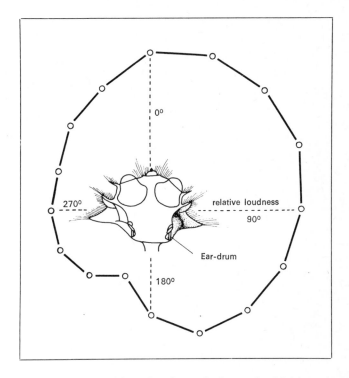

Figure 2. Directional field of the right ear of a long-eared owl (Asio otus). The feathers have been removed, the ear is shaded in. View of the head from above. The sound source (3,000 cycles per second) is circling horizontally around the owl's head. The actual loudness of the sound perceived is marked as the distance from the centre to the heart-shaped curve (dotted lines).

of the head, the time differences are correspondingly minute. It was long doubted whether the theory of perception of time differences could be correct, although many experiments suggested that it was. This way of hearing the direction of sound can, of course, only function properly if the two ears are not too close to one another. Song birds must, therefore, unlike owls, be content with the first mechanism and rely on the loudness of the sound for detecting its direction. Moreover the perception of time differences does not function–or functions only badly–if the sound is transmitted with a constant frequency and loudness. We all know how

Figure 1. Barn owl (Tyto alba) in flight with prey.

difficult it is to discover where a monotonous whistling comes from.

How can the central nervous system resolve such minute differences of time? If a source of sound is to be pin-pointed even a few more degrees accurately, then intervals of $\frac{3}{100,000}$ of a second must be registered.

A few years ago the Americans Galambos and Rupert, in collaboration with the German zoologist Schwartzkopff, carried out an interesting experiment on cats which has provided a profounder explanation of the whole problem. They investigated the activity of nerve cells in the auditory centres of the brain which, in the first instance, have nerve connections to both ears.

They discovered a remarkable type of nerve cell. These cells signal impulses to higher and superior centres in the brain only when the ear on the same side of the body is stimulated by a clicking sound. If the other ear is stimulated by a click before or at the same time, this click produces no effect. If, however, the far ear is stimulated shortly after the ear on the same side as the cell, the situation is quite different. If this delay is about $\frac{3}{10,000}$ of a second the nerve cell no longer reacts to the earlier click which sounded by the ear on the same side as itself. The probability of the nerve cell reacting is about only half as great. If the click by the far ear is from $\frac{1}{2}$ to $\frac{1}{1,000}$ of a second later, the nerve does not react at all. It only reacts again to its 'own' click if the interval between that and the next click near the other ear is greater than one thousandth of a second. Therefore time differences of only fractions of a thousandth of a second between the sound of

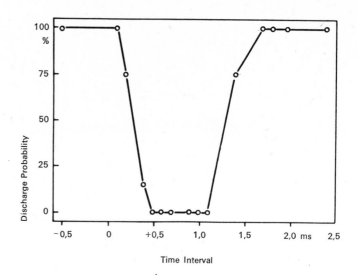

Figure 3. Probability of impulse formation in a cat's special type of nerve cell. Horizontal axis: time interval between a click at one ear which causes this cell to send signals and a second click at the other ear. If the second click is 0.5 to 1 thousandth of a second later the cell does not react. Vertical axis: discharge probability (percentage of the clicks which start a nerve impulse).

the clicks reaching the two ears determine whether or not the cell sends a signal to the highest auditory centres. When we remember that nerve cells of this type are numerous we can understand how intervals of $\frac{1}{10,000}$ of a second or even less can be measured. The number of impulses which are passed on average by all these cells together is a clear indication of the difference in the time it takes for sounds to reach both ears.

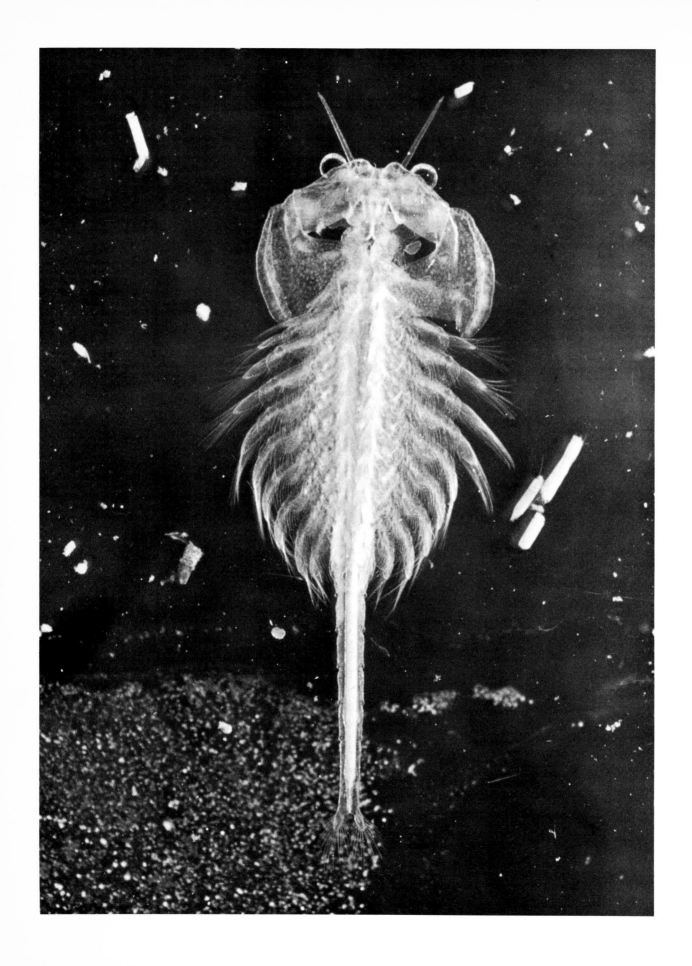

Gravity Orientation under Water

A school of angel fish *(Pterophyllum spec.)* swims past us—a picture of grave elegance. The movements of these fishes are assured and deliberate. To achieve this they need a reliable orientation mechanism. Light and gravity provide the data about their direction in space. The data travel via the eyes and organs of equilibrium into a system which regulates the position and movement of the fish in space. Not all organisms have well developed organs of equilibrium. Thus the brine shrimp *Artemia salina* shown in Fig. 1 orientates itself only by the direction of falling light, which normally coincides with the direction of the earth's gravitation. If, in addition, an animal possesses organs which show it the direction of gravity these often work in conjunction with the eyes.

We are indebted to E. von Holst for important discoveries about the functioning of these orientation devices in fishes. Let us take a closer look at the angel fish in our aquarium. We see a few fishes from the front. The tall, narrow bodies are upright, the vertical axis is perpendicular. Now we take the lamp which has been shining down into the tank from above and throw the light on the fishes from the side. They incline their bodies at an angle of α from the perpendicular and towards the light. This leaning is the result of simultaneous orientation by both light *and* gravity. The fishes remain in this position even in the face of disturbances like

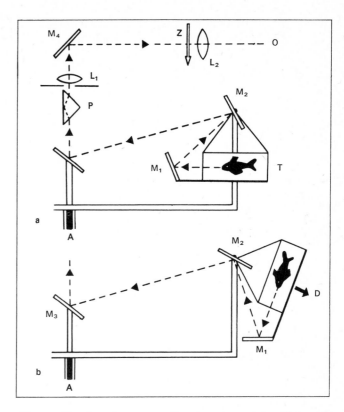

Figure 3. Experimental apparatus to investigate the sense of equilibrium of a fish under the effect of increased gravity. Explanation of the abbreviations in the text.

eddies. We say they are in a state of equilibrium in the light and gravity fields.

In fish, as in all vertebrates, the sense organs concerned with equilibrium in space are situated in the head, in a complex called the labyrinth. In higher vertebrates a part of this labyrinth has become the organ of hearing. In the labyrinth of a fish (Fig. 2) the most striking feature is the three semicircular canals which contain the sensory apparatus, the cupulae (Cu). They form a fluid-filled system of pipes into which the cupulae are built like swing doors. They respond when the fish turns. But because of their inertia the fluid stays behind and causes the cupulae to bulge.

While these organs respond specifically to turning movements, doing so quite independently of the fish's actual position in space, the organs of equilibrium do in fact supply information about the latter. They indicate position and change of position in relation to the direction of gravity. In the labyrinth (Fig. 2) we can see the three 'gravity stones' of a fish, also called statoliths—that of the utricle, the saccule and the lagena. Each one is attached to a cushion of sensory hairs, together with which it forms the sensory apparatus. The utricle is of especial importance for orientation in space. We still know very little about the importance of the saccule and the lagena. Now how does this organ of equilibrium

Figure 2. The labyrinth of a fish. Explanation in the text.

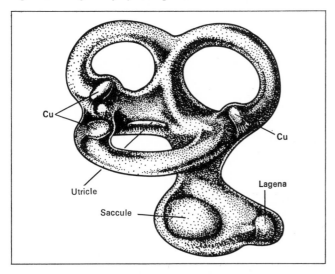

Figure 1. The brine shrimp, Artemia salina. The little shrimp keeps turning belly upwards when swimming. With its semi-spherical compound eyes, protruding near its antennae (at the top of the photograph), it perceives the direction of the falling light and sets its course by that. Natural size about 10 mm.

work? We can investigate the state of equilibrium of the fishes under the influence of increased gravity in an experimental centrifuge (Fig. 3). In the upper part (a) of the diagram the movable component can be seen at rest round the axis A. A cylindrical tank (T) is suspended from one arm, the other arm –not shown– carries a counter-weight. A system of mirrors (M), lenses (L) and a reversing prism (P) which revolves at half the speed allows the person carrying out the experiment (O) to observe the fish from outside. From the front he sees it as a stationary picture– even when the centrifuge is whirling round. A pointer (Z) can be made to coincide with the line of the vertical axis of the fish and the angle of incidence can be read on a scale. In the lower part (b) of the diagram we can see how the tank swings out when the centrifuge is working. It acts like a plumb-line, pointing in the direction of the effective gravitational force (D) which results from the superposition of terrestrial gravity on centrifugal force. The 'force of gravity' therefore attacks the 'bottom' of the tank. Consequently the direction of gravity remains the same for the fish and its environment; only the intensity changes. The value of the gravitational force is measured in multiples of terrestrial gravity. Normal terrestrial gravity = 1 g, twice terrestrial gravity = 2 g, etc. The faster the centrifuge revolves the greater the force of gravity becomes and therefore the heavier the fish and its statoliths weigh.

In a series of experiments we next determine the position of equilibrium with the light striking at the same angle (β) but under different forces of gravity, for example 1g and 2g (Fig. 4). As the influence of the light is the same in both cases, the result must yield information about the effect of gravity on the statolith organs.

Under the increased gravitational force the fish stands more upright and the angle α becomes smaller. The increase in the weight of the 'gravity stones' alters the amount of the excitation and this makes the fish aware that its position has changed. It attempts to correct this apparent change in order to maintain its original state of equilibrium. This correction aims, therefore, at keeping the excitation felt by the organs of equilibrium at a constant intensity.

The results of the experiment now allow us to draw certain conclusions about the way excitation is produced. Fig. 4 shows both the utricles with the forces affecting the statoliths. The downward pull of the force of gravity can be imagined as being exerted in two partial forces. The shear-

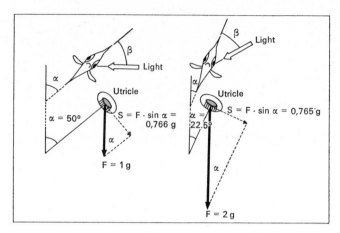

Figure 4. The position of equilibrium of a fish under different forces of gravity. Explanation in the text.

ing force strikes sideways, that is, parallel to the bearing area of the statoliths and the pressure force is perpendicular, pressing them down on the bearing. The relationships between shearing, force of gravity and the angle of incidence conform to the formula $S = F \sin \alpha$. From our experiments with various large gravitational forces we can now say that if the force of gravity is altered the fish adjusts its angle of incidence in such a way that the product of the gravitational value and the sine of the angle of incidence ($F \sin \alpha$) remains equal. That is to say the fish keeps the shearing constant, but not the pressure. In our example it sticks to a shearing of about 0.76 g. This investigation shows, therefore, that the shearing force is sufficient to stimulate the sense organs.

We spoke of the fish registering a change, a disturbance of its state of equilibrium. Its organs of equilibrium signal an increase in inclination sideways. This message results in an order to the fins to reduce the inclination. The execution of this order is again supervised by the organs of equilibrium. Thus the organs of equilibrium and the organs of movement interact continuously. And so we have before us a working unit which is comparable to an automatic control system. Components which both adjust and register position work together the whole time.

Our angel fish owe their orientation and movement in space to this sort of control system. Higher centres determine which direction shall be taken. That system then sets and maintains this course against disturbances in the way that has just been described.

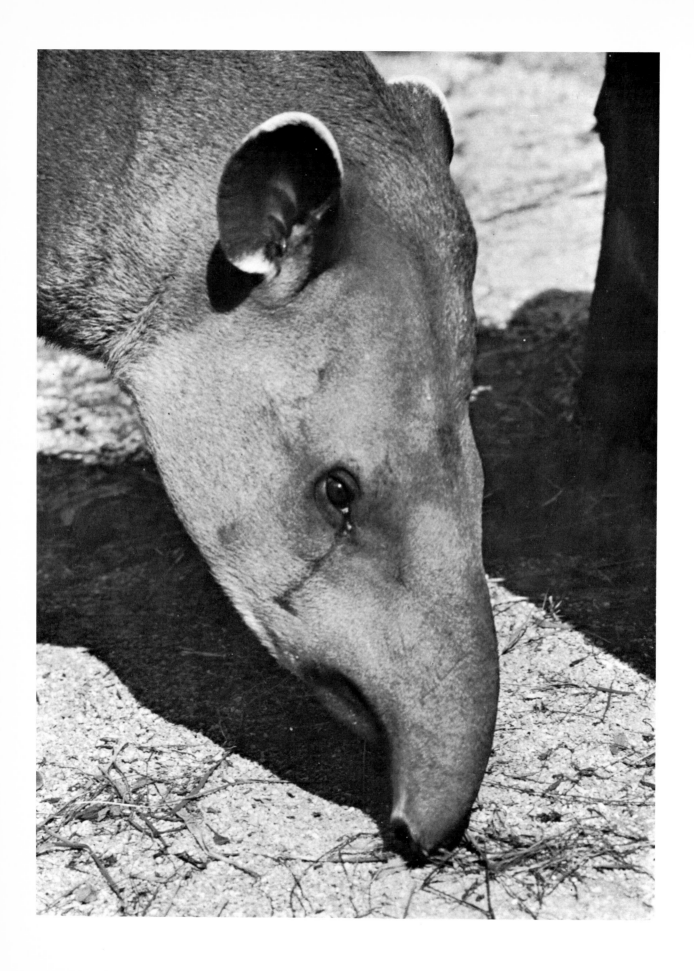

Location by the Nose

The colour photograph shows three zebras at a watering place. If you look more closely you can see that the nostrils are distended and that long hairs are sticking out of the soft skin in all directions. We all know from personal observation that horses, which are closely related to zebras, have a sensitive, soft-skinned and therefore exceptionally flexible muzzle. It is the receptive region for numerous stimuli from the environment. Receptors of stimuli are of various types, the astounding mechanical sensitiveness of the nasal region being perhaps the most striking.

The long, bristling hairs are receptors of mechanical stimuli. At their roots there are sensory cells which conduct impulses at every movement of the hairs to the central nervous system. But it is not only these hairs which make the muzzle a sense organ. Embedded in the connective tissue of the lips and nostrils are innumerable collections of sensory cells and nerve endings, each one a highly sensitive instrument with which the animal can examine objects. In this way the region of the lips and the nose performs part of the task which, in man, is done by the hand. The tactile sensitivity of the nasal region can, actually, be much greater. A proboscis or snout is an example of this sort of evolutionary development. This is very obvious in tapirs (Fig. 1). This development reached a climax in the animals which have trunks, of which the elephant is now the sole survivor from the many species which existed in past ages.

The nose is the most effective organ which zebras have for orientation in their environment. The many odours which reach them from far and near must be examined continually if the animals are to be safe from surprise attack by an enemy. The eye is comparatively far less useful for this purpose. Writing about zebras Fehringer says: "Zebra herds, often a thousand strong, like to graze peacefully with long-necked animals like ostriches and giraffes, whose all-round view they use as a periscope, just as buffaloes and antelopes also do; and, then, last but by no means least, there are the herons which like to perch on the backs of the animals as they graze, acting as 'look-out man'."

A definite part of the brain is linked with the nose, as it is with every sense organ. Here the impulses coming from the sensory cells are passed on to nerve cells. These interpret the impulses and convey the results to other centres. There the results are compared with data from other sense organs, undergo a further conversion and finally reach the systems which initiate the animal's response. It is illuminating to know that the size of a brain area which is associated with a definite sense organ matches the importance of that organ for the animal's orientation. For the more important it is, the more accurate the sense organs and the more connections there are with other systems, then the greater the number of nerve cells and nerve fibres and, therefore, the greater the size of the brain area. Consequently the brain of a horse has a relatively large olfactory bulb. On the other hand, the olfactory bulb is comparatively small in many apes which–like man–have become 'eye creatures' (Fig. 2). Fig. 3 gives an impression of the complex connections in the olfactory bulb.

Compared with what we know about the functioning of the eye and the ear, our knowledge of how the nose works is still very sketchy. The main reason is that it is very difficult to discover the precise nature of the process of stimulation. These difficulties need to be explained rather more fully. Air is drawn into the nasal cavity through the nostrils and it passes over the olfactory sensory cells. In animals with an acute sense of smell, like zebras, the surface of the inner nasal cavity is greatly increased by being in folds. Various glands secrete a fluid which is evenly distributed over the surface by fine ciliary hairs. These prevent the sensitive cells from being dried up by the stream of air which flows over them. At the same time foreign bodies which are drawn in with the air are flushed away. In addition, the molecules of odorous substances are trapped in the film of fluid.

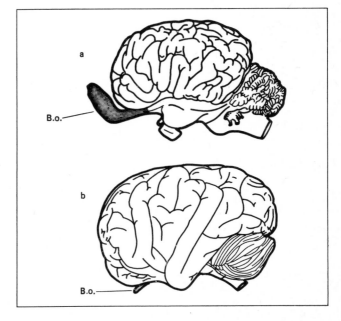

Figure 1. A young South American tapir (Tapirus terrestris). The short but extremely flexible snout is examining the ground.

Figure 2. The relative sizes of the olfactory bulb (Bulbus olfactorius, B. o.) (a) of a horse, (b) of a gorilla.

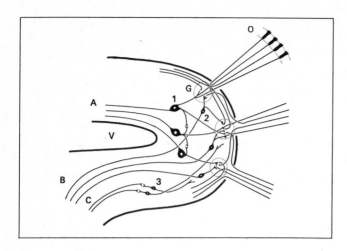

Figure 3. Simplified sketch of the fibre connections in the olfactory bulb (Bulbus olfactorius). The processes of the olfactory cells (O) extend to the olfactory bulb. There, near the surface, are the contact points (glomeruli, G) with the mitral cells (1) and the tufted cells (2). One bundle of nerve fibres (A) runs from the mitral cells to higher centres in the brain and another bundle (B) from the tufted cells to the olfactory bulb on the opposite side. Coming from there is the bundle of fibres (C) which are connected with the granular cells (3). V is the ventrical cavity.

At the surface of the olfactory cells the molecules of odorous substances, by their effect on a still unknown but highly sensitive receptor mechanism, start up processes in the olfactory cells which, as with all types of sensory cells, ensure that impulses are conducted along the extension of the cell to the nervous system.

There are, in fact, a very large number of odorous substances with a bewildering profusion of distinguishable 'shades'. Man has added a great many odours to the great number which nature produces and with which animals have to become familiar in order to be able to orientate themselves. Chemistry has synthesized a vast number of substances which do not occur in nature but to which the olfactory senses respond. The question that now arises is how the many substances are distinguished by the olfactory cells and their respective nerve centres. So far this is only a matter of theory. Early on an attempt was made to classify odorous substances into related groups. Actually many such substances in a particular type of odour are very alike. Thus flower scents can clearly be contrasted to musk-like types; further, putrid odours can be grouped together.

Several such categories have been differentiated. But it is difficult to discover molecular properties which are common to these related odours and which might be responsible for the stimulant processes in the olfactory cells.

Other methods are also being used in an attempt to break the 'code' which the sensory and nerve cells use to identify odours. By using fine electrodes it is possible to register the electrical 'answers' of such cells when these are stimulated by particular odours. The hopes of finding definite types of sensory cells which respond only to a certain number of specific odorous substances have so far not been fully realized. An idea which has been much discussed recently sees the geometrical shape of the molecules as the decisive factor by which the odours can be 'sorted out'. According to this theory, an olfactory cell responds only when the molecule of an odorous substance fits a depression of similar shape in the membrane of the cell. Just as similarly shaped keys fit the same lock, so odour molecules of a similar shape fit the same hollow in the cell membrane. But there are also objections to this theory. And it still does not explain which properties of the molecules actually affect the sensitive parts of the membrane. One can imagine it may have something to do with the oscillations in the molecule or with displacement of electrical charges in the membrane.

We have more information about the amazing sensitivity of the nose. Animals with a well developed sense of smell respond to a great number of odours which man does not perceive. Thus dogs, for instance, respond to a concentration of less than 10,000 molecules of butyric acid per cubic centimetre of air, while man can only detect a concentration which is a million times greater. The concentration value which just evokes a response is called the threshold stimulus. It is probable that the level of this threshold stimulus is determined mainly by properties of the olfactory centres. Experimental results suggest that even a few molecules of an odorous substance may suffice to make an olfactory cell generate impulses. Yet it is only when a large number of olfactory cells convey impulses to the nervous system that the responses of higher systems, and finally of the whole animal, are triggered off. When that happens the herd of zebra, warned by the odour of the enemy, can gallop off.

Colour Photograph. Zebras (Equus greyvi) at a watering place.

a

b

c

d

e

f

Insect Antennae

All insects have a pair of feelers, or antennae, on their head. Both the English and Latin words clearly define the significance of these organs. With them insects can touch or feel objects and so orientate themselves in their immediate environment. Like wireless aerials, insects' antennae pick up messages over a great distance and, used as direction-finders, lead their owners to the source of those messages. Finally, many insects understand one another by means of their antennae. Thus ants rapidly tap other inmates of the nest with their antennae and this is an order to give up some of the food supply the latter hold in their crops. The same signal is understood by greenflies which extract the protein from the plant juices they have sucked up and then secrete the remaining ingredients as a thick, sugary syrup. Some species wait until they are actually ordered to do this by an ant trilling. In return, as a sort of reward, the ants protect the greenflies. For long distance direction-finding the antennae are equipped with an ingenious combination of several tens of thousands of sensitive cells. Individual cells, or receptors, register the temperature, others the humidity and the carbon dioxide content of the air.

In bees the environmental conditions of the hive are modulated via their antennae, so that all the bees together act as a control circuit. Similarly, a thermometer in a living room regulates the central heating in the cellar so that the temperature in the room can be kept constant. In this particular case the bees themselves act as the heating installation. They are impelled by the receptors on their antennae to keep the interior of the hive reasonably cool by carrying in water and fanning their wings.

Some of the most important cells on the antennae are sensitive to odours, some to many different odours, others only to specific odours. This is particularly true of moths, including the American *Hyalophora gloveri*. The females produce a unique odorous substance in glands at the hind part of their bodies and this affects only the males of the species, who have highly sensitive cells on their antennae which respond specifically to it. In the case of the silk moth *(Bombyx mori)*, which has been thoroughly studied in this connection, probably only a few single molecules of the substance need to reach the males' antennae. The chemical formula of this particular odorous substance was established by Butenandt and his colleagues in 1959. It is a doubly unsaturated alcohol with the formula $C_{16}H_{30}O$. Other closely related species produce different substances to attract the males, which again possess cells that are especially sensitive to them. The creation of a unique odour and the males' great sensitivity to it enable the latter to track it down over a distance of several miles when the wind is blowing.

While the sense of smell possessed by the antennae is a long distance sense in these moths, it helps bees to orientate themselves in their immediate vicinity. They examine systematically a local patch of scent with their very flexible feelers and in this they orientate in respect to the source of odour. This could in fact be described as 'stereo-smelling'.

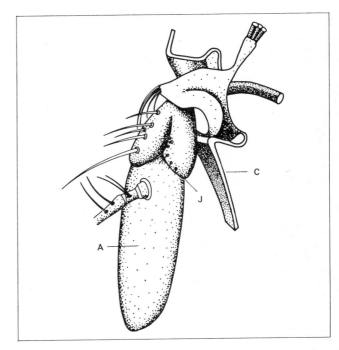

Figure 2. Large scale drawing of one antenna of a fly. Magnification about 50 ×. C: head capsule. J: joint in which part A of the antenna struck by the air current rotates against the upper part.

This ability is especially important for the life of the hive and for discovering blossom which is fragrant.

Where orientation is over a long distance the odorous substance reaches the antennae on the wind. Closely linked, therefore, with the efficiency of the antennae as organs which can smell things a long way off is the ability to detect air currents.

Air currents, whether caused by the wind or by flight, bend the antennae in a joint which is controlled by a large sense organ (Johnston's organ) (Fig. 2 and 3). The stronger the air current, the greater the forces in the joint and the

Figure 1. Examples of the many shapes of butterfly antennae. (a) Lobobunaea epithyrena from South Africa, male. (b) Female of the same species. (c) Perisomena caecigena from south-east Europe. (d) Female Spurge Hawk Moth (Deilephila euphorbiae). (e) comma butterfly (Polygonia c-album). (f) Female Small Heath (Coenonympha pamphilus).

higher the number of nerve impulses conveyed to the brain from the Johnston organ. The messages are passed on to the muscular system responsible for flight and this is so finely adjusted that the wings beat more slowly. Thus a control circuit is formed by which the flight speed can be kept constant in relation to the movement of the air.

Likewise, the flight course is stabilized by the antennae. Let us assume that part of a fly's wing has broken off–a misfortune which can befall an older creature. It would in fact now always fly in circles, since the sound wing generates more forward drive than the damaged one. In circling flight, however, the air current set up bends one antennae more than the other. In this case different instructions are sent to the two wings. The one which is beating too powerfully is immediately throttled down. As the control circuit in this

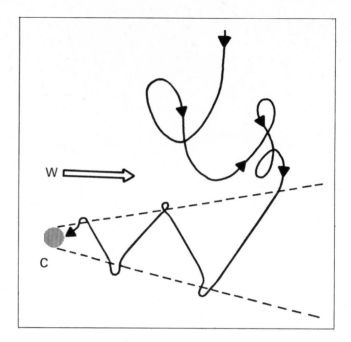

Figure 4. The flight course of the dung beetle (Geotrupes stercorarius) during its search for the source of an odour. C: cow pat. Arrow with W: wind direction. Dotted lines show the approximate limits of the odour trail.

way compensates the damage to the wing, the flight is kept straight.

The dung beetle *Geotrupes stercorarius* provides an amusing example of antennae co-ordinating their response to odour with their adjustment to the wind in order to locate something. In a wind this creature flies in a series of elipses or figures of eight against and across the wind until it comes on the odour trail of a cow pat. It then turns and flies diagonally across the wind until it finds that the odour has gone. There it turns once more and flies on again across the wind until it reaches the opposite limit of the odour. It zig-zags forward in this way until it reaches the cow pat. If the odour trail suddenly ceases–which is naturally what happens when the beetle is over the cow pat–it simply dives straight down. It usually lands right on the object of its desires and immediately buries itself in the dung.

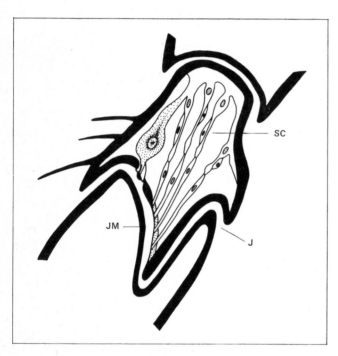

Figure 3. Section through the Johnston organ of a fly, magnification about 200 ×. JM: joint membrane. J: joint. SC: sensory cells which measure the state of the joint membrane.

Colour Photograph. Hyalophora gloveri (Glover's silkmoth, a North American Saturniid). The large feathery antennae, covered with many thousands of sensory cells are sensitive to odourous substances and wind direction and help the male to discover the female of the species at a great distance.

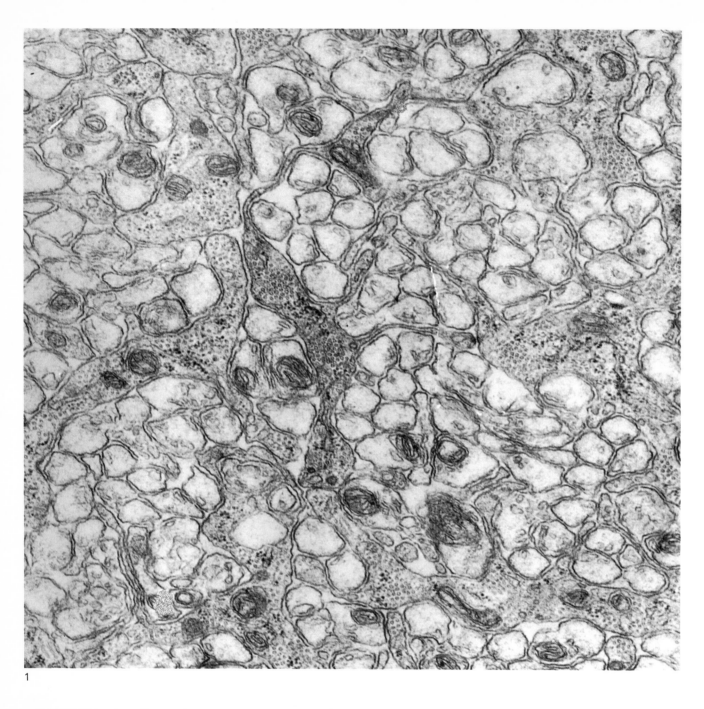

1

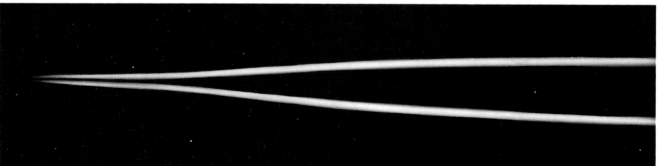

3

The Nerve as an Electro-Chemical Conduction Path

The task of an animal's nervous system is to co-ordinate the activity of individual parts of the body so that the organism functions properly in any given situation. The environment is constantly examined by sense organs and the activity of all the organs of the body is also supervised by countless, mostly small and inconspicuous sense organs. All messages about conditions of the external environment and in the body's organs are conducted to the central nervous system by afferent nerves. There the ever-changing flow of messages is evaluated and afterwards the effector organs such as muscles and glands are constantly activated and controlled through efferent nerves. About the middle of the last century it was discovered that the signals travelling along the nerves –the nervous excitation or nerve impulses as these are called in nerve physiology–are accompanied by fluctuations of electrical tension. At the same time the physicist and physiologist Helmholtz made the first successful measurement of the speed of conduction, which had hitherto been considered to be infinitely high. He found it to be 20–30 metres per second in a frog at room temperature. Nerve physiology made very great strides after 1920 with the help of modern electronic techniques using valves and transistors. A large number of experiments on all types of nerves of the most varied animal species has allowed us to build up a coherent concept of the conduction processes in the nervous system. Each nerve consists of a large number of individual nerve fibres, or axons, which are extensions of nerve cells (Fig. 1). The individual fibre, no matter whether it originates in an afferent (incoming) or efferent (outgoing) nerve, recognizes only one kind of signal for transmission – the nerve impulse. This is true of all animals. The amplitude of the nerve impulse is constant and measures about $\frac{1}{10}$ volt. Likewise, the duration of the impulse and the conduction speed in an individual fibre are of a constant value, though these vary for different fibres. In warm-blooded creatures the most rapid impulses last less than 1 millisecond–that is, one thousandth of a second; very slow impulses–for example,

in snails-last a few hundredths of a second. The conduction velocity lies between the extreme of 0.1 metre per second and 160 metres per second. The one thing which can change in the individual nerve fibre when it carries various messages is the rate at which the impulses follow each other. If the conditions are kept constant in the experiment the impulses in some nerve fibres succeed one another at extremely regular intervals. The fastest rate so far known is over 1500 impulses per second: but the upper limit is mostly a few hundred. More frequent than absolutely regular discharge-patterns are those in which the interval between successive impulses changes in a random manner around a mean value. If the conditions affecting a nerve fibre change as time goes on the impulse rate per second also changes. In impulse-free conditions a more or less rapid sequence can begin, an existing medium rate can become faster or slower, it can stop completely, and finally it can change periodically in a definite rhythm. The time sequence of the impulses is controlled at the origin of a nerve fibre. At points of contact with other nerve cells or sensory cells electric currents or chemical substances affect the nerves and change the rate. The task of the sensory cells is, therefore, to transform quantities measured by them, such as light, the concentration of a substance, temperature, pressure, sound etc., uniformly into processes which can affect the succeeding nerve fibres. In the same way control is also exercised over the effector organs. The impulse travelling along the fibres of a nerve cell releases at the point of contact with the effector organ chemical substances which modify the activity of that organ. This is comparable with the way many technical control and guide systems work. Non-electrical quantities, such as pressure, temperature etc., are first transformed into electrical quantities (current, voltage and resistance), then these analogous electrical quantities are measured and determine the flow of signals in the mechanism. In the same way the non-electrical quantities which are to be guided are influenced by electrically operated devices such as magnetic valves and the like.

Now how does an organism conduct impulses of only $\frac{1}{1000}$ of a second and of unchanged voltage at a speed of 100 metres per second along a cell process usually a mere $\frac{1}{100}$ mm thick and often several metres long? Today this basic question can be considered as good as answered. About 1930 an English anatomist, J. Z. Young, showed that squids have individual nerve fibres of almost 1 mm diameter which must, therefore, be particularly suitable for the investigation of conduction processes (Fig. 2). Two other Englishmen, A. L. Hodgkin and A. F. Huxley, who participated in the subsequent reasearch, made a vital contribution. In 1963 they were awarded the Nobel Prize for their work. Squids (*Loligo peali*, *Loligo forbesi* and *Loligo vulgaris*), swift, torpedo-

Figure 1. Electron micrograph of a cross-section of sensory fibres of the antenna nerve of the silk moth (Bombyx mori). The light sections are axons which come mainly from olfactory cells. They run in bundles which are more or less surrounded by glia cells (cells accompanying nerve tissue). Average diameter of the axons is 0.1 to 0.2 μ.

Figure 3. A micro-electrode for investigating individual nerve cells, greatly magnified. The tip–on the left–is so fine (1/10,000 mm) that it can no longer be resolved in the light microscope. On the right of the photograph the diameter increases to 15/1,000 mm.

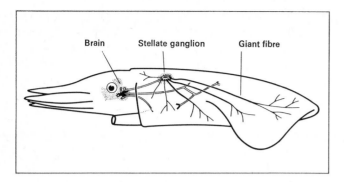

Figure 2. The system of giant nerve fibres of a squid (Loligo).

shaped molluscs were the subjects of the experiments. The colour photograph *(Octopus vulgaris)* shows a creature related to these creatures. With the giant fibres of the squid it is possible to insert one electrode into the fibres to investigate the nerve impulses (Fig. 3) while the second electrode is immersed into a fluid round the fibres (blood substitute solution). In this way all the electrical processes in the cell can be measured without any shunts. Between the interior and the exterior of the fibre there is always a potential difference of about 0.06 volt; this is called the resting potential. This potential comes about in the following way. The external solution contains mainly sodium chloride which, however, is separated into two oppositely charged elements –the positive sodium ion and the negative chloride ion. Inside the cell, on the other hand, there is a lot of potassium, positively charged like the sodium, and the ion partners in this case are large, stationary, negatively charged protein molecules. The concentration of ions on both sides of the membrane is, therefore, completely different. Now as all particles in a solution tend to distribute themselves equally, the chloride ions travel inwards and the potassium ions outwards across the surface of the cell. The corresponding ion partners are, however, prevented from crossing the membrane since the membrane in a state of rest is almost impermeable to sodium and the protein molecules are, in any case, held fast. The result is a surplus of positive charges outside the cell membrane and a negative surplus inside. The energy needed to maintain the electrical field over the membrane is supplied by the cell's metabolism. The fine balance between the differences in concentration and the electrical potentials is easily disturbed by electrical or chemical interference. In such a case the permeability qualities of the nerve membrane change dramatically. If the resting potential is lowered by a current flowing across the cell membrane, the membrane becomes more permeable to sodium and some sodium ions enter. If the influx exceeds a certain critical amount, the result is an explosive reaction. As positive charges then reach the inside of the fibre its membrane potential is reduced still further, the membrane becomes still more permeable to sodium ions and so on. In less than a thousandth of a second the membrane loses its charge and, for a short space of time, a reversed membrane potential builds up. So many sodium ions invade the inside that this becomes positive towards the outside for a short time. Measured from the resting value the change of potential is altogether about $\frac{1}{10}$ volt and the peak of the nerve impulse is reached. While this is happening, however, restorative processes are already beginning. After the increase in sodium permeability the membrane, after some delay, also becomes much more permeable to potassium. Then the membrane is again sealed against sodium, with the result that it gradually returns to a state of rest, a condition which is reached a few thousandths of a second after the start of the whole process.

Once an impulse is released at a definite point along the nerve fibre it is obliged to continue. The charge at this active point is reversed; that is, it becomes negative outside and positive inside. Consequently oppositely charged ions flow away from neighbouring, still undisturbed membrane areas. If, however, the membrane potential at these points is diminished in this way they, in turn, get caught up in the cycle of a nerve impulse. In this way a disturbance–the nerve impulse–once started travels along the whole nerve fibre. The speed at which it travels depends essentially on the electrical data of the nerve fibre: the smaller the resistance and the smaller the capacity, the quicker the charges can be reversed and the faster the impulse is propagated. The bigger the diameter of a nerve fibre the smaller its resistance, so that thick nerve fibres have higher conduction speeds than thin ones, provided that their structure is otherwise the same. The large nerve fibres of the squid have, therefore, compared with the creature's other nerve fibres, an extremely high conduction speed–about 30 metres per second. If they had a diameter of only $\frac{1}{100}$ mm they could carry impulses only at a speed of about 3 metres per second. This high conduction speed enables squids to co-ordinate their fast and powerful swimming movements.

Colour Photograph. The Octopus (Octopus vulgaris).

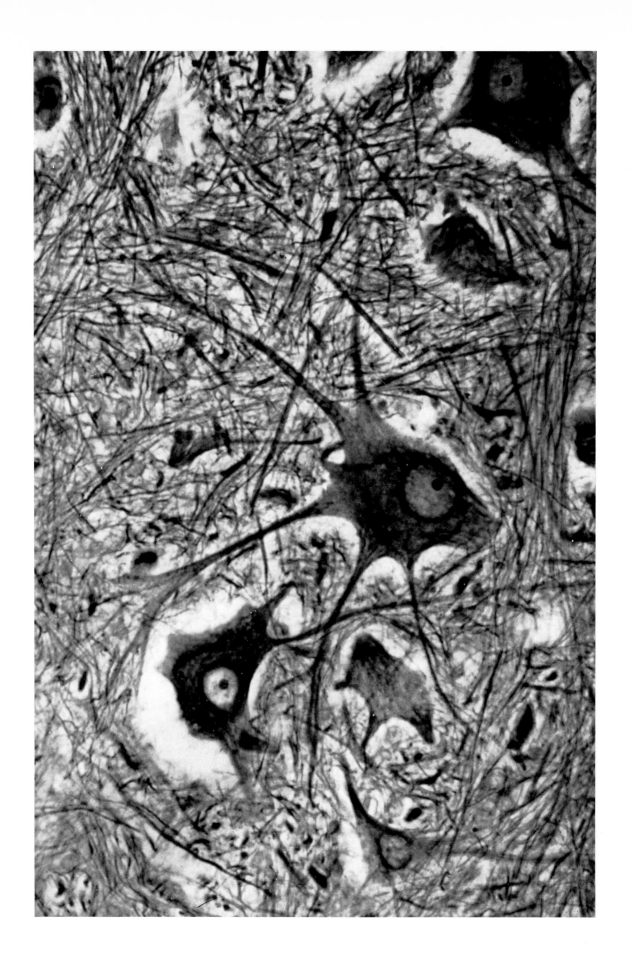

Motor Neurons

Nerve cells, or neurons, are the bricks from which human and all animal nervous systems are built. The round, elliptical or star-shaped cell-bodies have a long thin process, or extension, the nerve fibre. This carries the signals which travel to and fro over great distances in the nervous system at a speed of between 1 and 100 metres per second. The individual signal is a short electrical impulse lasting a few thousandths of a second and having a tension of one tenth of a volt. Nerves, which may consist of hundreds of thousands of such fibres, run to the brain and the spinal cord, continously conveying the information, which the sense organs receive, about what is happening both in the outside world and inside the body. Other nerves from the brain and the spinal cord activate the muscles and body organs by means of their impulses.

The nerve fibre knows only one form of signal—the nerve impulse, which has already been described. The messages and information coming into and going out of the nervous system are made up from the individual nerve impulses in two different ways. Firstly, a definite succession of nerve impulses travels along the individual nerve fibres (Fig. 2). A definite body of information corresponds to each of the possible time patterns. Secondly, the nerves consist of many individual nerve fibres. The distribution of impulses to the individual fibres offers a further possibility for the transmission of various messages. If, for instance, nerve impulses pass simultaneously along many of the fibres of a nerve leading to a muscle, the muscle contracts vigorously. If impulses travel to the muscle along only a few of the nerve fibres the muscle develops that much less power.

Thus the space-time pattern of the impulses in the many fibres of a nerve contains the messages. How do these patterns come about? How does the nervous system work? The colour photograph and Fig. 1 show motor neurons in the spinal cord. These are the nerve cells whose processes extend to the muscles. Whether or not a muscle contracts is ultimately decided by the many neurons linked to it. The more of them to send out impulses and the faster these impulses follow one another, the higher the tension developed by the muscle. The impulses originate at the place where the nerve process leaves the cell-body. But what decides whether, and in what sequence, impulses are formed? The cell-body of each nerve cell has additional short extensions which branch out like small trees and are, therefore, called dendrites. Now nerve cells are connected with one another by the terminal branching of the long or short cell processes touching the other cell (Fig. 3). At the points of contact, called synapses, one nerve cell passes information on to the next one. Whenever a cell sends out an impulse, a small amount of a powerful chemical substance is released at the points of contact with the next cell. At least two kinds of substance are released. One gives the receiving cell an urge to form an impulse, the other inhibits it. There are hundreds and hundreds of such contacts, covering almost half the surface of the cell-body of the motor neuron. Whether or not the cell finally forms an impulse or not depends on the actual flow of exciting or inhibiting urges at the time. If the flow of positive urges exceeds a fixed threshold an impulse is formed: if the flow rises still higher impulses are driven along the fibres at an even faster rate. If the flow from inhibiting contact points rises, the formation of impulses is slowed down or even stopped completely.

Figure 2. A succession of nerve impulses in a nerve cell of a crayfish. Height of the impulses about 0.1 volt, duration about 3/1000 of a second, frequency 20–30 cycles per second.

Figure 1. Motor neurons in the spinal cord of a cat, magnification about 500 ×. The cell-bodies of the ganglion cells are star-shaped; inside are the cell nuclei, looking like eyes. Cell processes (dendrites) branch out repeatedly. They and the cell-bodies are thickly covered with synapses, contact points with other nerve cells.

Now the many hundreds of contacts of a motor neuron originate in very varied sources. Some positive contacts stem from nerve fibres which run direct from the brain. A flow of impulses along this path, for instance, sets in motion a willed motor action, that is, a deliberate movement. Other influences affecting motor nerve cells do not travel via the brain. If a gnat stings us we always touch the place where we have been stung without thinking, that is, involuntarily. The sting has stimulated sense organs in the skin whose nerve paths, after passing through a few switching neurons in the spinal cord, terminate in the nerve cells of a group of muscles appointed at the time to play the major role. Thus our hand always aims for the right place without the brain thinking about it. Finally, there are in the muscle itself sense organs which are continually measuring its length. If this length deviates from a value given by the brain, the sense organs send impulses directly to the motor neurons of their own muscle, and these immediately change the length appropriately–providing, therefore, a control circuit which stabilizes the length of the muscles against disturbance and maintains the normal position of our body.

All the procedures described so far are positive urges for the nerve cells. Cross-connections in the spinal cord take care of the inhibiting influences. If the nerve cells of a muscle are forced into greater activity, the nerve cells of all the counter-acting muscles are simultaneously inhibited by these cross-connections. If muscles which bend a joint contract, then the muscles which can stretch the joint are simultaneously inhibited: that is, they relax and do not resist the movement.

This alternation between promotion and inhibition is automatically balanced by the connecting nerve cells of the spinal cord. The brain therefore needs to give only relatively simple orders via the nervous pathways which run to the spinal cord. The special pattern of signals for the muscles is then formed in the motor neurons of the spinal cord after the messages from sense organs of the skin, the joints and the muscles and the activity of all co-operating or counter-acting muscles have been taken into account. The many hundreds of tiny contact points, or synapses, of the motor

neurons are the switches in the signal-box which evaluates the vast number of incoming messages and decides what signal is to go out.

Figure 3. Sketch of a motor neurone. CB, cell-bodies. D, dendrites. NF, nerve fibres. MF, muscle fibres. N, interneurons. S, synapses (junctions with other cells). In the sketch the proportions are distorted. The cell-body is less than 1/10 mm in diameter, the nerve fibres 1/50 mm. In large animals the fibres can be several metres long. The terminal knobs of the synapses are 1/1000 mm in diameter.

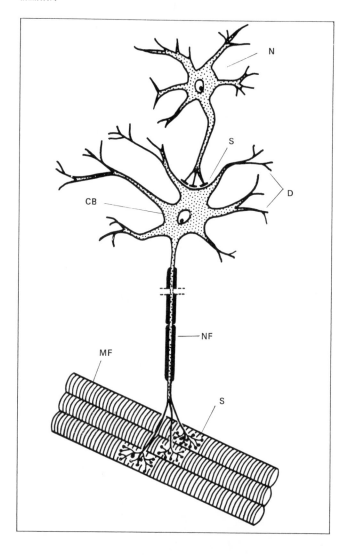

Colour Photograph. Motor nerve cells in the spinal cord of a cat (Felis domestica). (Section of tissue, magnification about 1500 ×. Taken from Fig. 1). The bright red cell-body is clearly visible with the surrounding network of fibres and cell processes (dendrites).

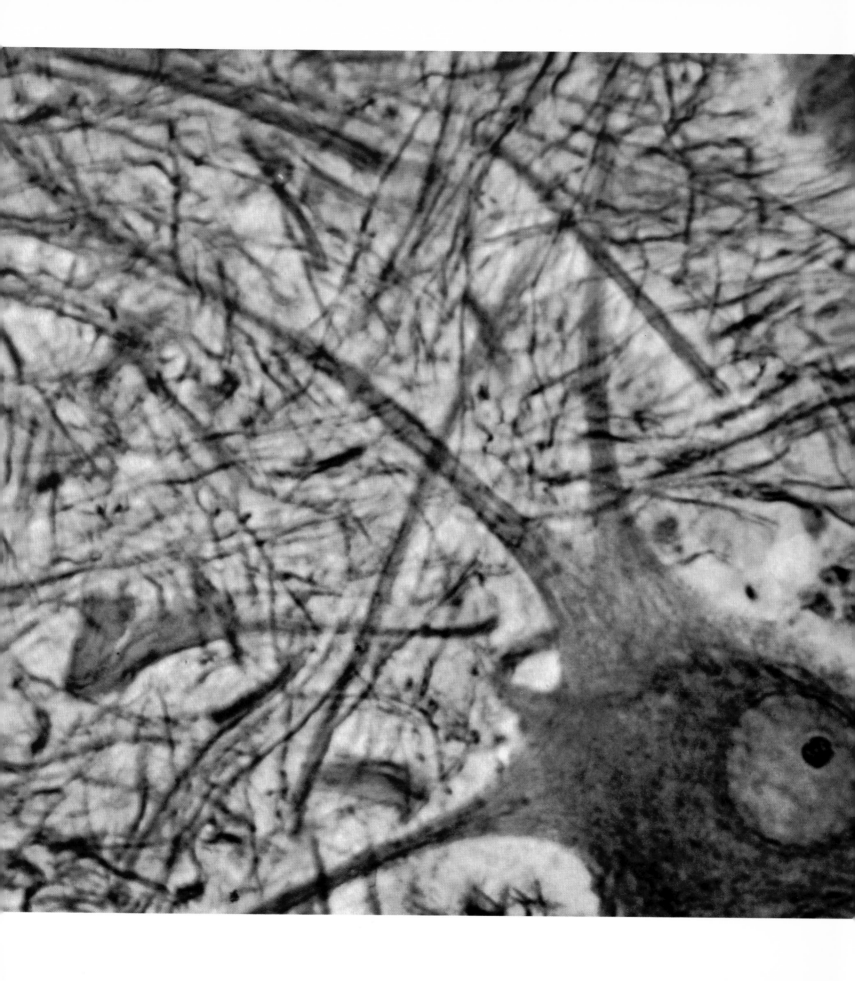

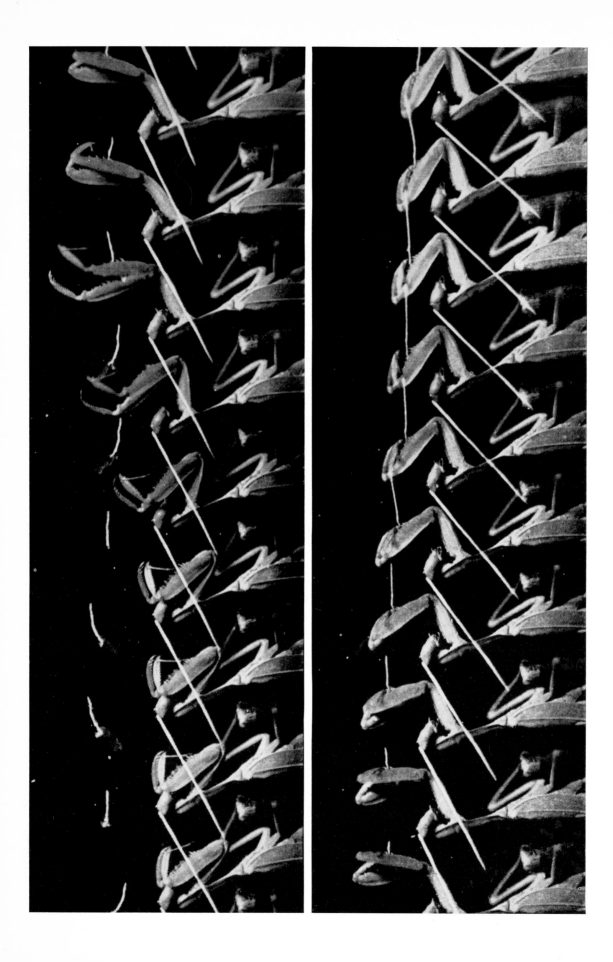

The Control Circuit in Aimed Movement

In the course of a day we make, quite unconsciously, a lot of movements which are aimed at various things. Time and time again we put our hand out to grasp a familiar object like a door knob. This movement is subject to a completely automatic optical control, for the eye registers every deviation of the hand to the right or the left and, after complex processes in the brain, it corrects the hand movement. This completes a cycle of action, forming a control circuit by which every deviation of the hand from the direct path to the door knob acts upon itself to reduce that deviation. The circuit is made up of the following phases: deviation from aim–eye–brain–correcting movement–diminished deviation from aim. It is easy to see how it works if we examine a rather silly sort of mishap which frequently occurs. It sometimes happens that a person puts out a hand to take the door knob but turns to speak to a companion before actually touching the knob. If, in the meantime, someone else has opened the door, the person often grasps thin air. In this case the active circuit was broken by the eye being taken off the knob. The action was completed in accordance with a previously set programme and no correction was possible.

Quite often the eye loses control of the course of the action for another reason–because the movement is made so quickly that any counter-order comes far too late. Many predatory creatures which attack their prey with a swift movement are in the same situation. There is, for example, the chameleon which shoots out its tongue to catch insects, or the praying mantis (shown in the colour photograph) which catches flies with its fore-limbs.

The praying mantis *(Mantis religiosa)* which is found in the Kaiserstuhl in Germany belongs to a group of insects which comprises some 1600 species and is widespread in the tropics. The name refers to the characteristic attitude adopted by these creatures when they lie in wait for their prey with their long, deadly fore-limbs folded in to the body in the posture of someone at prayer. As soon as a fly appears within reach, the praying mantis turns its head towards it and strikes like a flash with both limbs–much too swiftly for the fly to be able to escape. The victim is gripped between the creature's barbed femur and tibia and then devoured. The

whole operation takes only 30–50 thousandths of a second. It is so swift that the creature's eye, which is fixed immovably in its head, can no longer make any correction. Therefore everything depends on the precise course of the aiming process before the actual strike. H. Mittelstaedt has made this clear in a series of rather elegant experiments.

The mantis first fixates its prey. It turns its head towards it so that the fly is almost in line with an axis drawn through the middle of its head. This fixatory process is based on a control circuit, just as grasping the door knob is–the difference in the case of the mantis being that it controls only the aiming process before the strike and not the approach to the target. How is the direction in which the fore-limbs must strike determined? As the head can be moved freely with respect to the thorax, the animal must be absolutely sure how far it has turned in fixating its prey. The neck joint is, in fact, furnished with little cushions of sensory hairs which touch the back of the head and are differently bent and thereby stimulated when the head is in various positions (Fig. 2). These cushions therefore signal the head position. Surprisingly enough, this information is not used for directing the fore-limbs, as experiments to check this have shown. Instead it is used to make an asymmetrical contraction of the muscle system controlling the head position. This completes a second control circuit. Its job is to make every head position–once this has been ordered by the eyes–immune to disturbance from outside. It fulfills this subordinate control function brilliantly. This immediately becomes clear if the nerves leading from the hair cushions are severed, breaking the circuit. The amazingly high proportion of successes–85 percent–achieved by an intact creature drops to between 20 and 30 percent after the operation.

Now that the mantis has established that the order to turn the head has been carried out, it only needs to send a copy of this order to the fore-limbs. This copy must always correspond to the actual head position–a truly elegant solution of the problem which is rewarded by an 85 percent chance of success.

The newly hatched mantis larvae already feed themselves in the same way as the adults. They do not seem to have to learn by trial and error how to strike in the right direction. Otherwise they would presumably die of starvation during their apprenticeship. And so the delicate apparatus of eye and sensory hairs for measuring angles and the other parts used in the complicated control system that comes into play in the aiming process are already precise, accurate instruments at the moment of hatching out. With the praying mantis the art of catching flies is inborn.

Another predator, the archer fish *(Toxotes jaculatrix)*, a native of the shallow waters of South East Asia and some 10 cm long when fully grown, does not strike its prey with

Figure 1. How the praying mantis Hierodula seizes its prey. The insect hangs upside down. Pictures taken at intervals of 10 milliseconds. The sequence runs from bottom left to top right. The bait, a black cardboard disc, hangs from a white thread. The disc is seized between femur and tibia about 50 milliseconds after the creature has begun to strike. The two forelimbs are not finally withdrawn until 100–200 milliseconds later. A little balsa wood stick fixed to the head enables the head movement to be seen.

the same certainty as the praying mantis. It notices every insect or spider moving at a certain height above the water, swims just below the surface until it is nearly beneath its victim, turns upright into a firing position and spits a tall jet of water at its prey. If its victim does not fall into the water immediately, it can spit up to seven times in quick succession. When it shoots, its tongue is pushed up against the roof of its mouth, sealing a channel which leads into the firing tube. When the gill cover is closed suddenly the pressure in the mouth cavity increases so much that the water is shot out through the tube.

With the archer fish also success depends essentially on the accuracy of the aiming procedure before the shot. Unlike the praying mantis, the archer fish aims with its whole body. Positioning the body in such a way that it does not miss by shooting to the right or the left is much easier to control. But how upright must the fish actually be to allow for the movement of its prey, the changing range and the refraction of the water? By and large we still do not know whether the archer fish makes any corrections for these factors. But we do know that it has refined a method of increasing the probability of scoring a direct hit, by jerking a little more upright as it fires, thus achieving a greater vertical dispersal of its jet, which breaks up into single drops.

Figure 2. The mechanism of the aiming process in the Mantis.

(a) Diagram showing the co-ordination of the organs involved. E, eye. M, neck muscles. H, cushion of sensory hairs. L, fore-limbs.

(b) Diagram of the control circuit.

When aim is taken the eyes give the neck muscles an order to turn the head and its fixed eyes towards the target. The hairs stimulated by this movement seem to resist it for they tend to force the head back again, with the result that the head lags always a little behind the fly. This is, however, allowed for in the system. The task of this particular control circuit is to exclude external influences which would alter the position of the head, and it does this by giving counter-orders to the neck muscles.

a

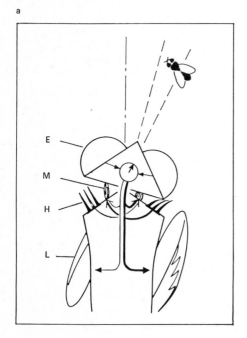

b

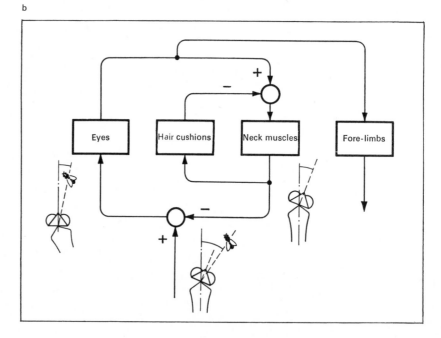

Colour Photograph. Praying mantis (Hierodula spec.) lying in wait for prey.

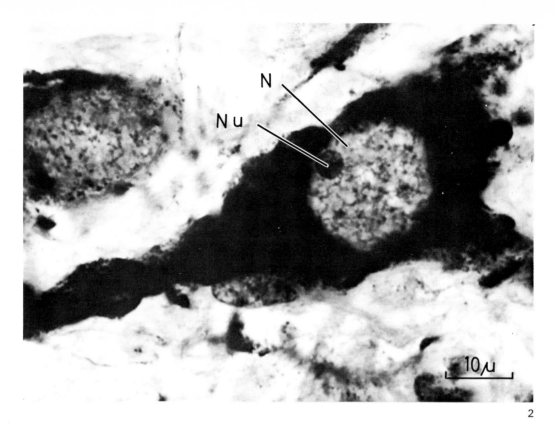

N

Nu

10μ

2

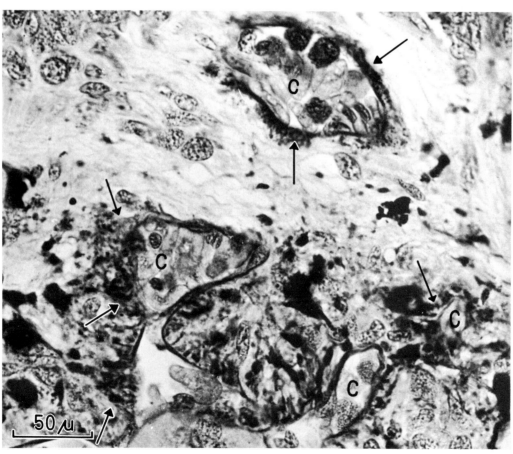

C

C

C

C

50μ

3

Messenger Substances in the Organism: Hormones

The activity of the individual organs of an animal's body is directed by two different kinds of signal. Rapid processes, such as the movements of the skeletal muscles, are started by electrical impulses which travel at great speed along nerves from the central nervous system to the effector organ. Many processes within the organism must, however, be delicately attuned to one another over long periods. Messenger substances, or hormones, often do this. These powerful chemical substances are produced in special glands, endocrine glands, and direct the activity of the organism and its parts over long periods of time. Growth and maturation are determined by hormones. Hormones govern the periodicity of the sexual functions, milk formation, the salt and water balance of the body, sugar metabolism and many other things. In most of these control processes come into play. If a particular function becomes over-active a corresponding hormone gland is automatically stimulated to change the hormone production in such a way that the function reverts to its norm. The best known example is perhaps diabetis, which is the result of a deficiency of the hormone insulin which is formed in the pancreatic gland and controls the sugar metabolism. Just as the higher centres of the brain control lower, more or less independent centres in the nervous system, hormone control of the function of the organs is regulated by higher hormone glands. The hypophysis, or pituitary body, of vertebrates is a control centre of this type. Fluctuations in the activity of lesser glands are notified to the pituitary body via the blood vessels or the nerves. This alters its activity in the production of such hormones, which now influence the subordinate glands. In this way a constant watch is kept on the hormone balance of the body. Very close inter-relationships with the nervous system exist simultaneously in the pituitary body, so that there is a close link between nervous and hormone control. As the hormones are carried to the effector organ through the blood-vessels, we find a close spatial agglomeration of gland cells, nerve fibres and blood-vessels. The latter espe-

cially form an extraordinarily complex system of loops and meshes. The colour photograph shows a section of the hypophysis of an eel, with the vascular system injected with Indian ink making a striking picture. In all vertebrates the pituitary body is situated on the underside of the brain. It consists of two parts, the anterior and posterior lobe (Figs. 1 and 4). The gland cells of the anterior lobe are connected to nets and strands which enclose the branched blood cavities. Grain-shaped particles–granules which can be stained with various substances and apparently contain hor-

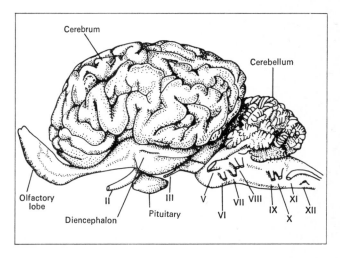

Figure 1. Side view of the brain of a horse. The pituitary body (hypophysis) is situated on the underside. I-XII, cranial nerves.

mones–can be seen in a light microscope. These are flushed into the blood through the cell membranes. Among the hormones of the anterior lobe, those which help to maintain the hormone balance of the body are especially important–for example corticotropin, which controls the adrenal cortex. This is a vital endocrine gland and governs the salt and water balance of the body. A further important anterior lobe hormone, thyrotropin, regulates the activity of the thyroid gland. Other hormones of the anterior lobe are engaged in the process of egg ripening and the formation of milk in mammals. Against the hormones which regulate the activity of other endocrine glands can be set others which directly influence the effector organs. One of these is somatotropin, which influences physical growth. Lack of this hormone results in a kind of dwarfism; conversely, over-production of this hormone results in gigantism. Unlike the hormones of the anterior lobe, those of the posterior lobe are not formed on the spot. The secretory granules originate in the brain, to be exact in specific nerve cells in the diencephalon. This process of secretion in nerve cells is called neurosecretion (Fig. 2). The granules

Figure 2. Microphotograph of a secretory nerve cell from the diencephalon of the black spiny dogfish (Etmopterus spinax). The closely packed secretory granules are dark coloured, making the cell-body look black. N, nucleus of the cell. Nu, nucleus particle (nucleolus).

Figure 3. Section from the posterior lobe of the pituitary body of a black spiny dogfish (Etmopterus spinax). In this preparation numerous neurosecretory nerve fibres can be observed. They can be recognized by the dark secretory granules, many of them ending (arrowed) at blood capillaries (C).

are transported in axons, long extensions of the secretory nerve cells, into the posterior lobe of the pituitary body, stored there and finally discharged into the blood (Figs. 3 and 4). The travelling of the neurosecretory granules can be demonstrated in a striking fashion. If the 'flow-bands'–the numerous nerve fibres which are gathered into a bundle–are severed about half-way, the active transport is interrupted at the point where the cut has been made. A large quantity of secretory material accumulates subsequently at the side which is turned towards the cell-bodies from which neurosecretory granules are released, and this can be shown in the section preparation. We observe, therefore, that there are two kinds of conduction in many nerve fibres. On the one hand there is the conduction of excitation which reveals itself when electrical impulses are passed on and on the other there is the conveyance of hormones, acting as a chemical remote control over bodily organs. Two hormones were shown to exist in the neurosecretory system. Both are protein substances of relatively small molecular weight. In the neurosecretory granules they are bound to a carrier and become separated probably only when they pass into the blood. Although methods of isolating these hormones have been developed and their chemical structure can be explained, and even though a synthetic hormone has been successfully produced, very little is known about the way these hormones work. They certainly play an important role in regulating the water economy of

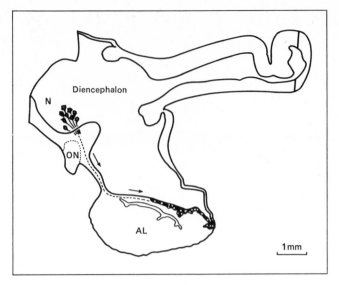

Figure 4. The course of the neurosecretory fibres (dotted line) in the brain of a lung fish (Neoceratodus forsteri) sketched in on a section from the brain. N, secretion-forming nerve cells in the mid-brain. The posterior lobe of the pituitary body is blacked in, the blood-vessels in it appear as white circles. AL, anterior lobe of the pituitary body. ON, optic nerve.

the body; and disturbances of the neurosecretory system gravely affect the functioning of the kidneys.

The achievements of the pituitary body seem even more astonishing when one considers how small it is. The human pituitary body is only about the size of a bean and it rarely weighs more than 800 milligrams.

Colour Photograph. The vascular system of the pituitary body of an eel (Anguilla anguilla). The blood-vessels are made visible by the injection of Indian ink and stand out in relief against the coloured mass of the tissue of the pituitary body.

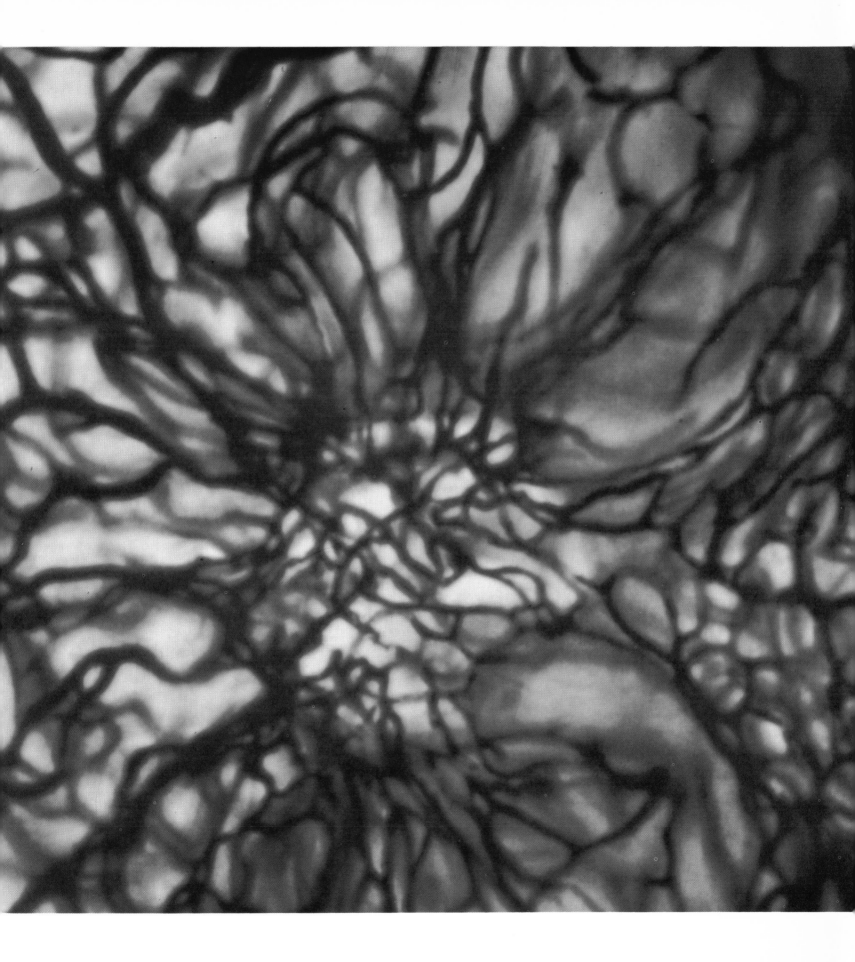

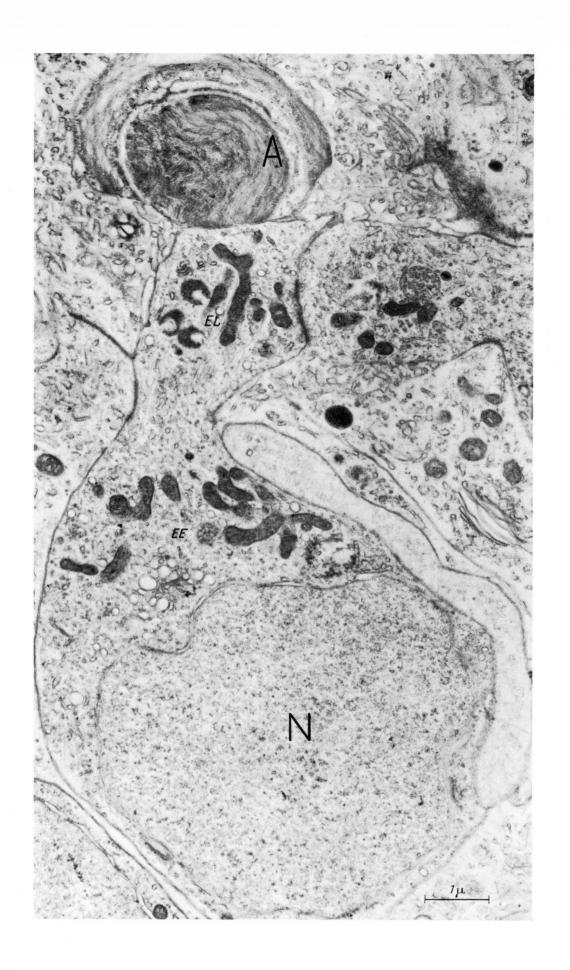

From the Third Eye to a Hormone Gland: the Pineal Body

The pineal body, also called the epiphysis, has probably excited more speculation than any bodily organ in the vertebrates. At last, quite recently, valuable knowledge about the complex basis of biological control processes has been gained from carefully devised experiments which were made in an attempt to explain the significance of this organ.

It is very difficult to fathom the exact function of the pineal organ because it is clear that a fundamental peculiarity of biological systems is involved, namely, the astonishing

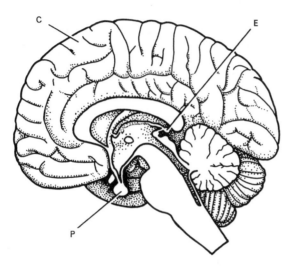

Figure 1. A longitudinal section of a human brain showing the pineal gland, or epiphysis, (E). Above it—as in all mammals—is the arch of the Cerebrum (C). In the lower vertebrates, fishes, amphibia and reptiles the epiphysis terminates just under the skull bone or immediately beneath the outer skin in an opening in the roof of the skull. Near the underside of the brain is the hypophysis, or pituitary body (P).

ability of each part of the body to change in the course of evolution. We always find the pineal body in the same place— as an outgrowth of a thin-walled area of the roof of the brain rising towards the forehead in the form of a conical, un-paired structure (Fig. 1). In lower vertebrates such as fishes and amphibious creatures it reveals, on closer exami

Figure 2. Electron micrograph of a visual cell in the pineal body of an edible frog (Rana esculenta). In the lower part of the cell is the large cell nucleus (N). The dark bodies in the narrower section above it near EE and EL are mitochondria, cell organelles, in which essential reactions of the cell metabolism take place. The cell terminates in the outer segment (A). Here the cell membrane forms a mass of extremely narrow folds in which the pigments sensitive to light are stored.

nation, the characteristics of an eye, a third, un-paired eye situated in the forehead and sometimes supplemented by other formations which all go to form what is also described as the pineal complex. Actually, it is not easily recognizable as such. In our common frog it lies concealed beneath the skin. A bright spot, deficient in pigment, between the large lateral eyes indicates its position (Colour photograph). In mammals, on the other hand, the pineal body is a gland which secretes a hormone and helps to control the hormone balance in the body. Only in mammals can the epiphysis rightly be called a gland as well, the pineal *gland*.

The existence of an un-paired structure on the upper side of a mammal's brain, which is otherwise characterized by having the essential parts arranged in pairs and recognizable externally, seems to have led the Greek physician Galenos, as long ago as the second century B. C., to speculate on the possibility that this structure may have a special significance. Later, the many-talented French philosopher René Descartes (1596–1650) further explored this train of thought. In his attempts to contrast the physical-mechanical working of the bodily functions with the independent activity pursued by thinking consciousness and to prove this conception of the nature of man by co-ordinating anatomical features, he ascribed a central significance to the pineal gland: in man he made it the seat of the soul.

What do we know today? In the lower vertebrates the pineal body is an efficient eye. Eyeless species of fish, even blinded fish, can be trained without much difficulty to respond to light stimuli which are received by this mysterious third eye. The question whether this eye functions in the same way as the lateral eyes is quickly answered. Photographs of the pineal body taken with an electron-microscope reveal visual cells of the same structure as those in the retina of the lateral eyes (Fig. 2), as well as nerve cells which are linked with the visual cells by synapses and from which fibres can be traced to the centres in the brain. Finally, successful attempts were made to register impulses from these nerve fibres. These experiments raised new questions. With frogs on the one hand, responses were recorded which were dependent of the wave-length. Short-wave light reduces the number of impulses passing over the fibres; long-wave light increases the number. In addition, however, a response was elicited which was found to be independent of the colour of the light. The curves of spectral sensitivity (Fig. 3) suggest the existence of a certain number of pigments which could, however, be at least very closely related to those of the lateral eyes (cf. p. 28).

But what do animals 'see' with these eyes which lie under the skin and possess neither a lens, nor an iris, nor even lids? Perception of objects in the external world is excluded because of the absence of these parts. For what purpose, then, is the information which is conveyed to the brain used? There is a theory which is soundly based, even though it is not yet proved–that the third eye could control the change of colour which occurs in animals (cf. p. 111).

Even the most searching investigation fails to reveal the existence of any visual cells in the pineal body of mammals. Instead, a characteristic cell form predominates, the pineal-ocyts. Another striking fact is the great abundance of blood-vessels, their delicate branches permeating the organ in addition to a close network of the thinnest nerve fibres which terminate in the individual pineal cell. This would seem to indicate that these cells produce and secrete specific substances into the innumerable blood-vessels, while the nerve fibres stimulate the production or the secretion of these substances. In point of fact experiments show that the pineal body of mammals functions in this way, as a hormone-producing gland which is subject to nervous control. Two questions must be answered. First, what substance is synthesized and what organ or system of organs does it affect? Second, where is the pineal body controlled? Melatonin was first isolated as an active substance from the epiphyses of cattle. Then it was shown to originate in the amino-acid tryptophane via a series of intermediate products. Evidence of its effect was given by experiments which were really designed to show how the activity of the pineal body is controlled. If female rats are kept under a constant light, the weight of the epiphysis decreases, but at the same time the activity of the ovaries is stimulated. Further experiments provided many proofs of these connections.

If light is shone on the lateral eyes, a specific excitation pattern is also transmitted along the fibres of the optic nerve to the involuntary or sympathetic nervous system. A sympathetic nerve establishes the connection to the epiphysis via a control point which is a ganglion in the region of the neck. As a result the production of melatonin in the pineal body follows a rhythmical pattern of changes, varying according to the changes of light through the day. Production falls by day and rises to a peak at night. It can be delayed by a change in the rhythm of the light: after the efferent nerves have been severed the rhythm is no longer transmitted.

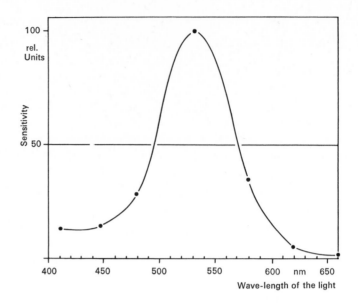

Figure 3. This curve of spectral sensitivity for the region of the pineal body of a minnow (Phoxinus laevis) - in relative units, vertical axis, was obtained by using light and food conditioning. The tested wave-length band is marked on the horizontal axis. The highest sensitivity occurs at 532 nm, that is in the band of light which to us looks green. Similar curves were obtained with frogs by evaluating impulses from the nerves of the pineal body.

Understanding of the connections is certainly made difficult by the fact that the amount of an intermediate product formed in the melatonin synthesis, serotonin, varies according to the photoperiodic light change, while the rhythm is maintained in permanent darkness. The light, therefore, synchronizes a rhythm established in the organism only by acting as a time giver. It becomes clear how closely the various control systems here are geared to one another. The sense organs register the lasting changes in the environment and pass on the information to the nervous system, where it influences the rhythm of the control processes and is finally concerned with delayed activity of remote organs via messenger substances (hormones)--with a success that is still unexplained. Up to now we do not know for sure how the activity of the ovaries is altered by a hormone of the pineal body. But there is every reason to be excited about the prospects for new discoveries.

Colour Photograph. A light spot can be seen between the eyes on the forehead of the common frog (Rana temporaria). Here, beneath the skin, the terminal vesicle of the pineal body lies as a simple third eye which has developed neither lids, nor lens, nor pupil but which still possesses typical visual cells.

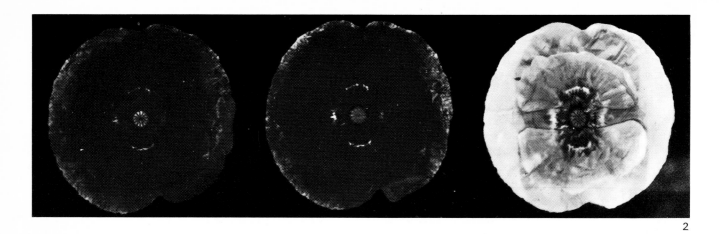

2

3

4

How does a Bee see Colour?

Nobody can experience what a bee feels when it catches sight of a summer meadow in flower. Nevertheless we do know how bees see the colourful world of flowers. In 1913 von Frisch devised a means for asking this question. He fed some bees on water sweetened with sugar on blue paper and then offered them blue paper without any sugared water along with lots of different pieces of grey paper of the same size. The bees settled only on the blue paper and proved, for one thing, that they had learned that the blue paper was a food signal and, for another, that they had recognized the signal by the actual colour and not just because it was a certain brightness.

Coloured pieces of paper are ill suited for more exact analysis. Therefore bees were trained with coloured lights of varying wave-lengths and intensity in a special apparatus for mixing the colours of the spectrum. By conducting a whole series of experiments it was possible to investigate the colour system of bees just as this had been done with people from the time of Helmholtz. Likewise flower colours can be understood objectively by measuring the reflections from the petals in the different spectral bands. Putting these two investigations together gives us an insight into the colours of the bees' world.

The spectral band perceptible to bees (300–650 nm) is biased towards the short-wave zone compared to that of man (400–800 nm) (Fig. 1). Bees are blind to red but they see ultra-violet rays as very bright, vivid colours. The red poppy, which reflects ultra-violet very strongly, appears to them in an ultra-violet colour tone which we naturally cannot imagine (Fig. 2). Dark red roses look 'black' to them because there is no ultra-violet reflection. The clouds of white blossom on our fruit trees, hedges and fields reflect almost no ultra-violet. Bees see them as coloured, in fact as

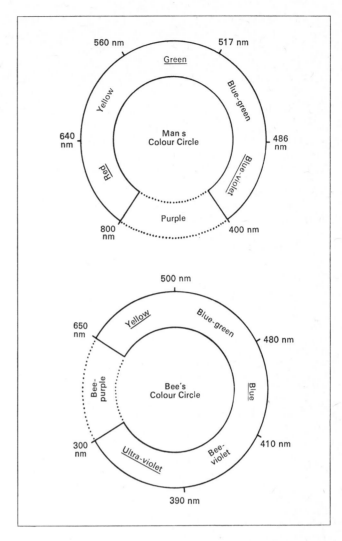

Figure 1. The colour circle of man and bees. Both colour systems are trichromatic. The three basic colours are underlined. By additive mixing it is possible to produce the intermediate colours. Complementary colours appear opposite the basic colours in the diagram. The main difference between the two systems lies in the shift of the spectral band visible to bees towards the shorter wave-lengths.

Figure 2. The reflection from the flower of a poppy in the bee's three basic colour bands. From left to right photographs taken through yellow, blue and ultra-violet filters. In addition to the red visible to us, the flower strongly reflects the ultra-violet visible to bees.

Figure 3. From top to bottom, the yellow cruciferous plants treacle mustard (Erysimum helveticum), rape (Brassica napus) and charlock (Sinapsis arvensis) photographed (left) through a yellow filter and (right) through an ultra-violet filter. Because of the absence of ultra-violet reflection, bees see the mustard as 'yellow'; because the ultra-violet reflections from the rape and the charlock are of different strengths, they see them as two different tones of 'bee purple'.

Figure 4. (From top to bottom) The yellow flowers of the mimulus (Mimulus), the creeping cinquefoil (Potentilla reptans) and the ragwort (Senecio Fuchsii) (left) photographed through a yellow filter, (right) through an ultra-violet filter. The access to the source of nectar is marked by a colour signal in the ultra-violet band invisible to us. It looks 'yellow' to bees in a 'bee purple' setting.

'blue-green', the complementary colour to ultra-violet. They reveal this by confusing white light free of ultra-violet with blue-green stimulus light with a wave-length of 490 nm. The rich range of orange, yellow and green colour tones which our eye perceives in the 650–500 nm wave-band look very much alike to bees. They easily confuse even orange and green. On the other hand different ultra-violet reflections from yellow flowers conjure up for them an unsuspected wealth of colour. The three yellow cruciferous plants treacle mustard *(Erysimum helveticum)*, rape *(Brassica napus)* and charlock *(Sinapsis arvensis)* they see as three quite distinct tones of colour (Fig. 3) which are again beyond our ability to imagine. It is the same with blue and violet flowers, in which ultra-violet reflections of varying intensity produce no less than six distinct colour tones for bees.

A yellow dandelion in a green field looks to us miserable as a signal to invite visitors which can hardly distinguish between yellow and green. But in the bees' world the field is simply not green. In the whole spectral band visible to bees, the reflections from the blades of grass are in fact all equally weak, so that they look 'uncoloured', 'grey' to them. And so for the bees for which they are intended, the brilliant signals of the flowers stand out most effectively against the uniform greyness of their background.

Even orientation on the flower itself is guaranteed by signals which are largely hidden from our human eyes. The entrance to the food source usually reflects no ultra-violet and stands out for the bees because it is of a contrasting colour from the periphery of the flower (Fig. 4). Even worker bees, which are inexperienced in flowers, suddenly stick out their proboscis when they overshoot such a signal. This shows that they have instinctively understood the message which the signal holds for them: "This is the way in to the nectar. Get your proboscis ready to suck it up." And even though it has no personal experience, every bee knows and follows the information proclaimed by a colour signal from a distant flower: "Come here! I've got something for you." On the other hand bees have no instinctive preference for colours. But they are able to learn individually each colour of a flower which is laden with food. The scent signal is, of course, the most important feature of the flower for, unlike the colour signal, it can be carried in the hair and communicated to other bees (cf. p. 99). In spite of the great differences between the colour perception of bees and man, there are fundamental functional features which are common to both

(Fig. 1). Light which contains all the wave-lengths of the spectral band visible in the same energy distribution as found in the unchanged daylight is seen by both bees and man not as coloured but 'neutral', 'colourless' or 'white'. If, for example, light is without the short-wave band, this appears in the complementary colour: with man it appears in yellow (complementary to blue-violet), with bees it is in 'blue-green' (complementary to ultra-violet). In man and bee the two extreme ends of the actual visible spectral band join the colour circle through a series of mixed colours (purple or 'bee purple'). The colour systems of both are trichromatic: that is, all the colour tones, including the 'colourless' ones, can be produced by three colours–in man these are red, green and blue-violet, in bees they are yellow, blue and ultra-violet. According to Helmholtz, laws of colour mixing can be explained on the assumption that there are three receptor systems of overlapping spectral sensitivity. Recently the existence of the three receptor systems postulated, with a maximum sensitivity in the yellow, blue and ultra-violet bands, was proved directly by recording from single cells electro-physiologically.

By this experiment the validity of the theory of colour perception developed by Young and Helmholtz a hundred years ago for man was immediately shown to hold good for bees as well. Electro-physiological experiments showed that the visual cells sensitive to ultra-violet accumulate in those parts of the eye which look upwards. Perhaps this has something to do with the still largely unexplained ability of bees to recognize the sun, the most important signal for orientation by the use of the sky, through a covering of cloud.

Colour Photograph. Bumble bee (Bombus spec.) at the Alpine eryngo (Eryngium alpinum). Bumble bees and honey bees see colours in much the same way.

a

c

b

d

Flower Colours as Signals for Insects and Birds

By a signal we usually understand a simple sign which contains a message. Thus a red traffic light means "Stop!" If we see signs bearing large printed letters hanging down from overhead tramway wires we ignore them for we do not know what they mean. Perhaps they are a signal for the driver? Two things, therefore, underlie the concept of a signal. Firstly, it is directed at a very definite group of people or animals. Secondly, the receiver must know the significance of the signal and must, therefore, have come to an agreement about it with the sender.

Animals and plants also recognize signals. Animals learn the significance of signals either in the course of their individual lives or they possess this knowledge instinctively, as an inheritance handed on from generation to generation. The development of definite and suitable signals on the part of the sender, the selection of definite animal species as the receivers and the development of inborn knowledge of the meaning of definite signals is the result of natural selection. If an individual, because of some chance modification of his hereditary structure, sends out a signal which is better understood by the receivers, this brings a slight advantage for the maintenance of the species. In the same way a receiver who understands the signal more quickly will have a slight start on his rivals. Examples of this kind of advantage are better food, more numerous offspring, a greater chance of survival or becoming more widely distributed. In the course of the history of the race (evolution) these small advances, taken together, eventually result in great changes. That is how the special signals and agreement on their meaning have evolved over millions of years. A good example is the interplay which takes place between plants and animals in the matter of visiting flowers and blossom. Stationary plants need carriers who will help in pollination and in the dissemination of spores and seeds. Besides the capricious wind and water, as a reliable means of transport there are animals. They carry pollen from plant to plant and thus take care of fertilization. They carry seeds away and thus ensure their dissemination. To prevent this from being a pure matter of chance they must be attracted by the plants. The plant offers the animal food and by means of striking shapes, colours and scents it signals that nectar and

fruit are there for the taking. In addition plants, rather like pirates, also put out false flags as signals (cf. the chapter on 'Orchids and Mimicry', p. 79 ff.). The odour of carrion attracts many insects which think that a carcass will provide a source of food for themselves and their progeny. Instead they find a stinkhorn fungus which uses this trick to help get its spores disseminated. Although the arum and the stapelia (Fig. 1b) and other flowers employ similar disreputable methods, the signals of flowering plants are generally of a more friendly nature. Pollination is guaranteed if one and the same animal visits lots of flowers of the same species one after another. Many plants therefore specialize in attracting a definite animal species and then, in return, this species looks only for these flowers. An example of this is the common fig, *Ficus carica*, which has specialized in a gall fly, *Blastophaga grossorum*. But faithfulness to one flower is mostly achieved by something rather like conditioning. Once recognized by the bees as a rich source of food, the same plant species is visited over and over again until the source is exhausted. To make recognition easier most plants have their own characteristic signal–a special shape, a particular colouring, an individual scent or some combination of these. An example is the flower of the charlock and the treacle mustard which look to our eyes to have the same shape and the same yellow colour but are two completely different signals for bees. The charlock reflects ultra-violet, the mustard does not (cf. the chapter 'How Does a Bee See Colour?' p. 71). As bees can see ultra-violet clearly, the first flower appears to them as a mixed colour of yellow and ultra-violet, which the zoologist calls 'bee purple', while the other looks pure yellow. Ultra-violet is an important signal colour for insects in general, since their eyes are very sensitive to it (cf. p. 23). On the other hand insects, with few exceptions, such as some butterflies, cannot see red. Blazing red, therefore, hardly ever occurs as a colour in our native wild flowers. But what about the corn poppy? This only appears to be an exception, for in addition to the red visible to us it reflects the ultra-violet visible only to bees. This can be seen from Fig. 2, p. 70.

In the tropics and the sub-tropics, however, one finds a considerable number of flowers which are magnificently and dazzlingly red–the flaming salvias, *Hibiscus*, *Amaryllis*, *Aloe*, Indian cane and many others. These are the flowers which are pollinated by small birds. The most well-known flower birds are the humming birds *(Trochilidae)* which live in America and are related to our swifts and the honey-sucking birds *(Nectariniidae)* of the Old World. But flower visitors are also to be found among many other families of small birds in the tropics and the sub-tropics. If one compares the sensitivity of a bird's eye to different spectral lights with the eyes of human beings and of insects (Fig. 2), then red proves

Figure 1. Grass pollen, as for example the pollen of the grass Uniola latifolia (a) is borne away by the wind. The carrion flower Stapelia variegata (b) attracts flies. Bats disseminate the pollen in the case of the cactus Pilocereus guentheri (c). The flowers of the clematis are visited by bees.

to be a very suitable signal colour for birds. The greatest sensitivity of the eye of day birds occurs at 600 nm, that is in the orange part of the spectrum. For them red is a particularly bright colour. Most bird flowers, not all red by any means, give off no scent, at least not one perceptible to us. As birds have only a poorly developed sense of smell, scent does not seem to be a suitable signal for them. As flower pollinators the humming birds play a major role, especially in the tropical regions of America. In many of these they seem to take over the whole role of insects. And so it is anything but astonishing that intensely brilliant and vivid red flowers are to be found in hundreds of plant species in the tropics.

After insects and birds the mammals constitute a third group of flower visitors. A few flying marsupials and bats have specialized in doing this and many plants also send out signals for them (Fig. 1c). The flowers of bat plants which open at night, are either very bright or plain and dull, but irrespective of this they give off a damp, sour or mouldy odour. This is the signal for the fruit-eating vegetarians among the bats. We do not have nocturnal flower visitors which flit like ghosts through the night and our native birds do not visit flowers. If they were to specialize in doing this they would find sufficient food only during a short season. Yet we can easily observe orange-red signals which are meant for birds. As well as the rowan-berries intended especially for them there are dozens of other fruit berries which are coral red. This signal tempts our birds to eat them. The indigestible pips are dropped in different places and so the diffusion of the plants is ensured.

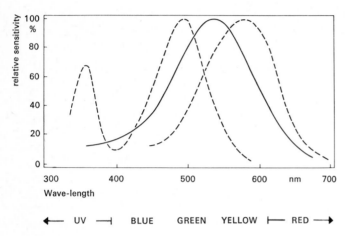

Figure 2. The relative sensitivity of different eyes to pure spectral lights. Vertical axis: relative sensitivity expressed as a percentage of the maximum sensitivity. Horizontal axis: wave-lengths investigated, in nm. Solid curve: sensitivity of the human eye in daylight. Broken curve (right): sensitivity of the eye of a pigeon. Broken, two-peak curve (left): sensitivity of the compound eye of a fly.

Colour Photograph. White tailed humming bird (Boissoneand jardini) at the flower of a Heliconia jacquinii, a species relatea to the banana.

a

b

c

d

Orchids and Mimicry

Orchids are among the most expensive and most beautiful flowers in the world, but they are also some of the most sophisticated in the way they get their pollen disseminated. Plants are actually older inhabitants of our earth than animals. But the vast array of coloured flowers that now exist could not evolve until there were enough animals to act as pollinators. Beforehand, plants had to depend on the caprice of wind and water. These carried the pollen anywhere and for nothing, but did so in a haphazard way. If pollen is to reach a definite recipient in this way immense quantities must be despatched. Animals, however, operate much more accurately, just as a postman is a more reliable agent for delivering a letter than a bottle which is flung into the sea with a letter in it. By using animals, plants can economize on pollen but they must reward the bearers for their services. Animals are not content just with something that is pretty to look at. They are interested in other things and flower colours are a very striking way of attracting animals to the contents which are their real concern.

Insects are by far the most numerous of the pollinators. In the first place plants offered the insects some of the pollen which was saved. In the case of *Cassia* this is carried to such an extreme that in addition to the stamens which produce normal pollen for fertilization purposes there are special stamens which hold pollen-like foodstuff just for the insects. But the majority of plants offer nectar. This too is the reward gained by about two hundred species of birds which act as pollinators. The plants, however, specialize in one or other of these carriers. 'Bird-flowers' have no scent (see p. 75), while 'insect-flowers' have distinct and very varied scents. Scents really mean very little to birds, but for insects, scents and colours are of equal importance. When one considers the amazing variety of these inducements it is obvious that they have not been created for us, although they often give us great pleasure. Many scents and odours are hardly perceptible to us and we do not see the same splendid wealth of colour in flowers because, unlike insects, we cannot see ultra-violet light. It is only when we photograph these flowers through an ultra-violet filter that we can, in a round about way, make the wide range of colours, but not the actual colours themselves, visible to us (see p. 71).

When the plants want their pollen to be carried to one of their own species they can offer a supply of nectar to the greatest possible number of pollinators. The only drawback is that other plants do the same and the bearers do in fact fly with the pollen from flower to flower, but not necessarily to another flower of the same species. That, however, is the only place where the pollen can fulfil its purpose. If the bearers visit all accessible flowers indiscriminately the flowers are no better off than when pollination is carried out by the wind. Therefore many of the more highly specialized varieties are designed to ensure that the pollen is disseminated with a definite recipient in view. Many flowers bloom only at certain times of the year, many only at certain times of the day. Species which flower only intermittently do not compete for pollen. Moreover, some flower visitors are kept away by the actual structure of the blossom. In flowers which have long corollas, for example, only butterflies with their long probosces can reach the nectar. Most flowers also exploit the learning powers of their visitors, which prefer to go on looking for a colour pattern which first rewarded them with nectar. Then it is a matter of evolving a flower pattern which is markedly different from those of competitors. And the wealth of glorious colour which delights us is the result of the breeding of distinguishing features which for many flowers that grow near one another are as important as a definite address is for people who live in large cities.

But many flowers exploit not what insects can learn but what they already know. Well-known examples are evil-smelling flowers, whose stench attracts beetles and flies which are searching for carrion. Flies even lay eggs on such flowers but naturally these perish. The visitor often finds nectar, but never the flesh it was after. Yet when it leaves it takes pollen which it faithfully delivers when it alights again on the next flower which promises rotting flesh. These carrion flowers use a false signal. They deceive the insects, which fail to learn the difference between real and decoy carrion because they often find even the genuine thing occupied and, frustrated, must fly on in a further search. There must be some sort of device—for example nectar—for teaching animals new signals. If a signal already known is used, however, the teaching device is dispensable. That is what these flowers do. They only smell of carrion: they never provide it—and yet visitors come, collect pollen and even deliver it to the right place because carrion flowers are fairly rare and therefore confusion is unlikely. The actual flower is often reddish brown, like rotting flesh. It may even generate heat. In the end it is just as arduous for evolution to deceive insects as it is to supply them with food.

We find the most beautiful examples of this among the orchids. Some are perfectly normal flowers containing nec-

Figure 1. The flowers of four species of orchid of the genus Ophrys: (a) O. apifera, (b) O. tenthredinifera, (c) O. fusca, (d) O. sphecodes. Magnification about 8×.

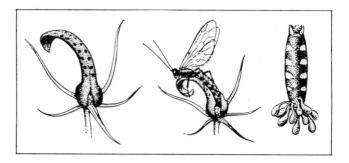

Figure 2. (a) Fly orchis Ophrys insectifera with the wasp Gorytes mystaceus. Left, flower; centre, wasp visiting the flower; right, head of a wasp with pollinia sticking to it.

(b) The wasp Lissopimpla semipunctata on the orchid Cryptostelis leptochila. Left, flower; centre, the wasp visiting the flower; right, hind part of the wasp with pollinia sticking to it.

tar. The specialists, however, like the orchis species of the genus *Ophrys* (Fig. 1), deceive 'their' insects but, unlike the carrion flowers, have a very select circle of visitors. The English names (bee orchis, fly orchis), like the Latin names for the species (for example *insectifera* = insect-bearing) inform us that the coloured parts of the flowers, in fact the labellum, look like the insects named. In this case, however, the similarity is not accidental, as it is with the skullcap, larkspur or snake wood, but so to speak deliberately intended.

These flowers were for a long time considered to be curiosities. Then it became clear that bees and bumble bees avoid them just as they avoid flowers which are already occupied by an insect. It is even possible to scare bees off normal flowers by fixing on them the blossom or even just the labellum of the fly orchis. It was difficult to imagine why the *Ophrys* species should frighten visitors off instead of attracting them. Darwin, who also studied these flowers, showed that they depend on pollination by insects. He wrote that a Mr. Price had often observed a bee attacking the bee orchis, and added that he could not imagine what this meant. Today we know, for several naturalists have simply observed what happens to these flowers. The fly orchis (Colour Photograph Fig. 2a) is visited only by the wasp *Gorytes mystaceus*, and even then exclusively by the males. And these do not attempt to find nectar–there is none–but they clasp the labellum with their legs, bend the hind part of their bodies inwards and make efforts to copulate as though they were covering a female for mating. Male *Andrena* bees behave in the same way on an *Ophrys fusca*,

Eucera males on *Ophrys arachnites*, males of the ichneumonid *Lissopimpla semipunctata* on the Australian orchid *Cryptostelis leptochila* (Fig. 2) and so on. This shows unmistakably that these orchids play a definite role as female decoys and are in fact visited in error by the males of an insect species. Kullenberg was able to prove this by further experiments with decoys. He found that even to our noses the faint scent of these flowers is like the sexual scent of the female insect which is imitated and has an aphrodisiac effect on the males. The latter can actually be stimulated to courting and searching flights by this imitation scent.

While the male is making vain attempts to copulate with the labellum it cannot help knocking against the pollen masses, or pollinia, of the flower which then remain hanging from its body on their stalks. The fly orchis is a decoy which has its head end in the middle of the blossom. With *Cryptostelis* on the other hand, the end of the labellum which is nearest to the blossom acts as the hind part of the decoy. Consequently the *Gorytes* male sits with its head towards the flower and gets the pollinia stuck on its forehead, while the *Lissopimpla* male sits with its head outside and carries the pollinia away on the hind of its body. This very sophisticated method employed by orchids, offering the visiting male insects not nectar but simply the opportunity of copulatory attempts has, however, a disadvantage. It means that each orchid species is completely dependent on the insect species which it has selected. That many orchids are moving largely in the direction of self-fertilization is probably due to the fact that they have extended their distribution area beyond their insect's area.

Colour Photograph. Flower of the fly orchis Ophrys insectifera.
Magnification about 15×.

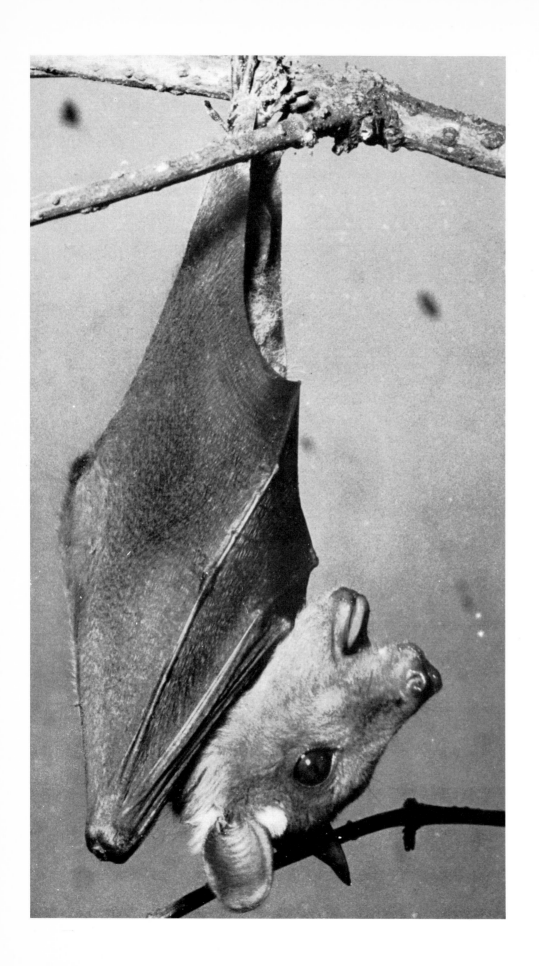

Echo Location at Night

While night birds, such as owls, can no longer fly in complete darkness or, if forced to do so, crash into objects, bats are expert flyers even in the pitch dark. They hunt prey and avoid obstacles with the greatest skill. This ability was studied by the naturalists Spallanzani and Jurine as long ago as 1793 and 1794. After conducting a series of very cleverly thought-out experiments they came to the conclusion that bats must find their way about in the dark with the help of their ears. Spallanzani also observed that the bats he was investigating were unable to steer a safe course if their mouths were plugged up. At that time there was still one outstanding problem to be answered–how could these silent flyers use their ears for orientation? Spallanzani's researches were completely forgotten and it was another 150 years before this question was answered, almost simultaneously, by the Americans Griffith and Galambos and by the Dutchman Dijkgraaf. The night-flyers send out a compact beam of ultra-sonic orientation sounds of high intensity and measure the position and distance of obstacles and prey by the echo which is reflected back from between 1 and 6 yards away. The pattern of the sounds transmitted and the way in which they are produced varies with the individual species. With most species, however, the basic frequency lies somewhere between 30 and 100 kilocycles per second: very rarely is it more or less. A few bats–in contrast to the majority of species which possess a highly specialized larynx– produce the ultra-sonic sound by a movement of the tongue –for example the Egyptian fruit bat *(Roussetus aegyptiacus)* and other fruit bats. The sound is emitted through the mouth, except in the case of the horseshoe bats *(Rhinolophidae)*. With them the nose acts as a directional transmitter. The sound is bunched and beamed through the horseshoe-shaped fold round the nose. The position of this can be changed as required by means of muscles. For short distance orientation a wide cone of sound is radiated, for a greater distance a highly concentrated sound beam is produced.

A number of bats, such as the *Vespertilionidae*, transmit very short orientation sounds lasting only two thousandths of a second. An analysis of recordings shows that each cry drops from a frequency of almost 100 kilocycles per second at the beginning to only about half that towards the end. When the bats are hunting for prey these sounds are repeated irregularly from 10 to 30 times a second. If a bat becomes

aware of an object the frequency rate of the impulses rises to over 100 cycles per second. The mouse-eared bat *(Myotis myotis)* native to our country belongs to this *Vespertilionidae* type. With the horseshoe bats the individual sounds last considerably longer, almost $\frac{1}{10}$ of a second, and while these are being sent out the basic frequency remains constant– about 90 kilocycles per second. The rate at which the sounds follow one another is more rapid, for the horseshoe bat transmits almost without a break. In Fig. 2 the two types of sound are shown together. Fig. 3 shows the frequency rate of the orientation sounds of a *Myotis* species when flying in search of prey. There are a number of intermediate forms between the extreme types which we have discussed in detail.

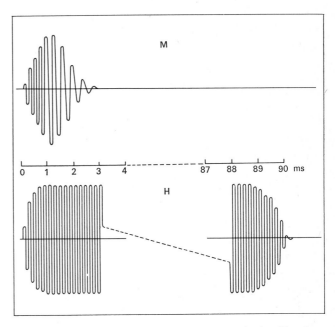

Figure 2. Orientation sounds emitted by a Myotis species (top) and by a horseshoe bat (bottom). The number of wave trains per pulse has been reduced to one tenth for diagrammatic reasons.

The pressure of the sounds uttered by the bats is extraordinarily high–between 20 and 60 microbars (μb) at a distance of 2 to 4 inches from the head. By way of comparison a compressed air hammer produces a sound pressure of 60 μb in the frequency range audible to us. The strength of the echo coming back to the bat is naturally much smaller, but bats can still pick up an echo which has a sound pressure of $\frac{1}{1000}$ to $\frac{3}{1000}$ μb. These figures mean that an echo can still be evaluated if its sound pressure is only $\frac{1}{10,000}$ of that produced by the signal which was transmitted. Nor does a high level of interference prevent them from navigating a safe course. It is true that the creatures then no longer hunt, but if they are alarmed they can still avoid objects, even if an interference of 20 μb is superimposed on the signals they send

Figure 1. Epauletted African fruit bat (Epomophorus wahlbergi) a species which has not the ability of echo location.

out. They are, therefore, able to filter out the echo which is a thousand times weaker than the interference. But we still do not know what the mechanisms are which make such a high insensitivity to interference possible.

Detection of a reflecting object is facilitated by the large and often highly flexible ear muscles. The horseshoe bats in particular constantly move them to locate prey and other objects. The method of doing this is probably different in the two types. Bats with echo direction-finding of the *Vespertilionidae* kind, like our mouse-eared bat, use both ears for detecting direction; the horseshoe bats need to use only one ear. In the first case it is probably the difference in time or intensity between the echoes reaching the two ears which is evaluated: in the second, the direction is discovered from the echo which returns with the greatest intensity by means of direction–finding movements. The method of measuring the distance of objects so accurately is still problematic. Future experiments must test the theories which have so far been advanced.

Some numerical data will show the accuracy of this method of orientation by picking up echoes. Fine wires between $\frac{1}{100}$ and $\frac{1}{10}$ of an inch thick are recognized as obstacles at a distance of 1 to 3 yards. Minute fruit flies *(Drosophila)* weighing less than $\frac{1}{1000}$ of a gramme and only $\frac{1}{10}$ of an inch long are detected from a distance of 1½ feet. In one experiment a little brown bat *(Myotis lucifugus)* caught ten of these flies a minute. The bat's reaction is so quick that it flies only 4 inches before altering course. As bats can manoeuvre on the wing with extraordinary skill the echo distances are quite big enough for them to be able to snap up prey or avoid an obstacle. Anyone who has ever seen a slow-motion film of bats in flight will never forget the experience. Every few seconds, in a series of breath-taking swoops and loops, they catch one victim after another from a whole swarm of insects. Should there ever be too little time to snap up a fly with the open mouth, it is swept up by the wing tips and whisked into the mouth. What looks to us just a mad whirl in the twilight air is, in fact, an acrobatic hunt.

Moths, a favourite prey, have their own form of defence. A furry covering absorbs the sounds emitted by the bats and becomes an acoustic camouflage. An organ of hearing sensitive to ultra-sonic sound gives warning of an enemy. If the moths are struck by one of these orientation sounds they

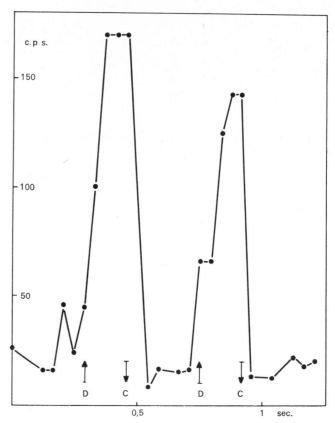

Figure 3. Echo location of fruit flies by the bat Myotis lucifugus in flight. Horizontal axis : time in seconds ; vertical axis : number of orientation sounds per second. After the detection of a fly, D, the number of sounds emitted per unit of time is greatly increased. After the fly has been caught, C, the number of signals decreases again.

fold their wings in a flash and drop. Moreover, bats are not only insect hunters. There is one species which catches fish. It, too, uses an ultra-sonic method of locating prey lying just below the surface of the water. Finally, many bats are fruit eaters and visit flowers, and only a small number of species live by sucking blood. The fruit and insect devouring vampire *(Vampirus spectrum)* is not one of these.

And so these ghost-like nocturnal creatures which have inspired so many legends prove, on closer acquaintance, to be for the most part useful insect catchers or harmless vegetarians. They are little flyers equipped with radar-like apparatus whose sensitiveness and efficiency are astounding even in our sophisticated age which is accustomed to technical marvels.

Colour Photograph. Mouse-eared bat (Myotis myotis) flying in search of prey.

Electric Location by Fishes

Long before man was able to explain the nature of electricity he knew it as a phenomenon in fishes. Even the ancient Egyptians knew about the powerful shocks that came from the electric catfish *(Malapterurus)* shown in the colour photograph, and the Greeks and Romans used the shock from the electric ray *(Torpedo)* therapeutically in the treatment of various illnesses. But it was not until the eighteenth century that the shocks were recognized to be of an electrical nature, and in the period which followed, especially in the second half of the nineteenth century, the fundamental discoveries about the structure and function of the electric sense organs of fish were published. The electric eel *(Electrophorus electricus)* has probably the most powerfully developed electric organ known. It accounts for 58% of the total body weight and consists of two specially adapted

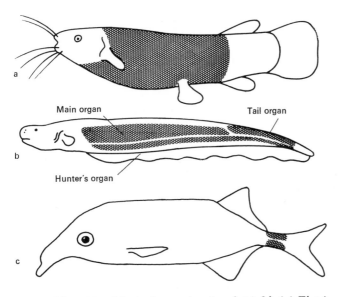

Figure 1. *The position of the electric organs in various electric fish. (a) Electric catfish (Malapterurus electricus), cf. Colour photograph; (b) Electric eel (Electrophorus electricus); (c) A tube-snouted mormyrid, Gnathonemus pictus. cf. Fig. 2a.*

strings of side muscles which run the whole length of the body (Fig. 1b). These strings of muscles are in fact a bundle of columnar structures which, in turn, are made up of some 5,000 or 6,000 smaller units. Each one of these minute units can generate a tension of 0.1 volt. Differences in the con-

centration of potassium, sodium, chloride and organic ions are responsible for the creation of this potential. Here we find the same processes operating which we met when we were considering the formation of impulses in the membrane of nerve cells (cf. p. 52). Nerve endings make contact to one side of the electric cells. Impulses travelling from the brain along these nerves trigger off the discharge of these cells. The basic units in the columns are arranged in series, like batteries, so that the individual charges all add together when they are released simultaneously on a command from the brain and can total up to 600 volts, which are maintained for a few thousandths of a second. The strength of the current rises to 0.5 amperes–enough to light an electric bulb if the wires are connected to the head and tail of the fish.

Up to a few years ago it was assumed that the fishes employed their electricity only to immobilize prey or as a form of self-defence against enemies. There are, however, a number of fish species whose electric organ is far less efficient, producing tensions of only a few volts, certainly not enough for it to be considered a suitable weapon for capturing prey or for defending themselves. The two types of organ are found together in the electric eel (Fig. 1b). The main organ which runs the whole length of the side of the fish's body and the so-called Hunter's organ underneath react by discharging 600 volts only if called on, whereas the electric organ enclosed in the tail is live all the time, but builds up impulses with a tension of only a few volts.

In the last fifteen years Professor H. W. Lissmann of Oxford has made a special study of 'low-voltage fishes', especially the African mormyrid *Gymnarchus niloticus*. This fish sends out electrical impulses almost continuously, even when it is resting and comparatively inactive. Fig. 3 shows the great regularity of these electrical discharges. The average impulse rate is about 300 a second, the tension between 3 and 7 volts. During the individual discharges the tail of the fish becomes negative–the opposite from the head (Fig. 4). Further investigations showed that low-voltage fishes are extraordinarily sensitive to electrical fields or to fluctuations in the electrical potential in the surrounding water. They possess a sensitive electric sense organ which, in the mormyrid for example shows even a gradient in potential of 0.03 microvolt per cm, or current densities of 0.04 microamp per square centimetre. Even the electrical charge produced

Figure 3. *The electrical discharges of the mormyrid Gymnarchus niloticus. The individual discharges of about 5 volts lasting only one thousandth of a second appear as vertical lines on the recording. They are repeated in regular succession at a rate of about 300 impulses per second.*

Figure 2. *A number of small 'low-voltage fishes', belonging to the mormyridae family. (a) Gnathonemus pictus (cf. Fig. 1c); (b) G. schilthuisiae; (c) Petrocephalus bovei.*

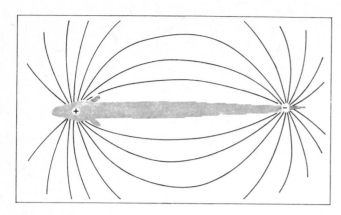

Figure 4. *During the discharge the tail of the fish becomes negative – the opposite from the region of the head. In a medium of overall equal conductivity the field of current produced is that shown in the diagram – the electrical field of a dipole aerial.*

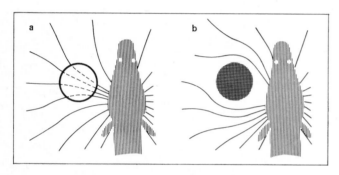

Figure 5. *(a) Objects which are good conductors – in the experiment, e. g. metal rods, in nature, animal bodies (higher salt content than fresh water) – draw the lines of flux together. (b) Objects which are poorer conductors than fresh water – air bubbles, stones, glass rods used in the experiment – push the lines of flux away from their immediate vicinity. The current density in such areas is less than in the undisturbed field.*

in a comb pulled through one's hair is sufficient to start a reaction in this fish.

In further experiments Professor Lissmann was able to show that the mormyrid can use its electric sense organ to detect and locate disturbances in the electrical field set up by its own discharges. Even from a distance of a few centimetres this fish can perceive a glass rod 2 mm in diameter because of the changes in the electrical field round it. The lines of flux are pushed further apart or bunched more closely together (Fig. 5) according to whether the object near the fish has a higher or lower conductivity. Consequently the

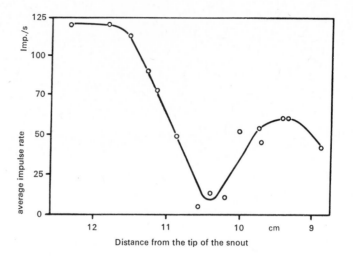

Figure 6. *The curve shows how the formation of impulses (vertical axis: number of impulses per second) in one of the fibres of the nerves along the lateral line organ of a knife fish (Sternopygus) depends on changes in the surrounding electrical field. A small silver plate is moved along the side of the fish (horizontal axis).*

current density changes in the skin of the fish's head and body, where the electric organ is found.

In the last few years a research group from the Zoological Institute of the University of Los Angeles has shown that sensory cells in the fishes' sideline organs respond to changes in the electrical field surrounding them. The question of how the sense organs codify these changes has not been fully explained. The reason is not only that different types of sensory cells have been observed already in only one fish, but also because the individual fish species differ from one another in this respect. One type of cell is, however, regularly found–a cell which conveys impulses to the central nervous system when the electric organ discharges itself. With changes in the surrounding electrical field the impulse rate of such cells changes in a specific way (Fig. 6), enabling a fish to detect and locate any disturbance. For the *Gymnarchus niloticus*, which inhabits muddy, almost opaque waters, this detection system is admirably suited for locating the objects in its immediate vicinity, including any prey. Many observations carried out on low-tension fishes also suggest a second hypothesis–that the electrical signals could be a means of communication between members of the same species, enabling them to establish agreed territorial boundaries.

Colour Photograph. Electric catfish (Malapterurus electricus). Fig 1a shows the position of the electric organ.

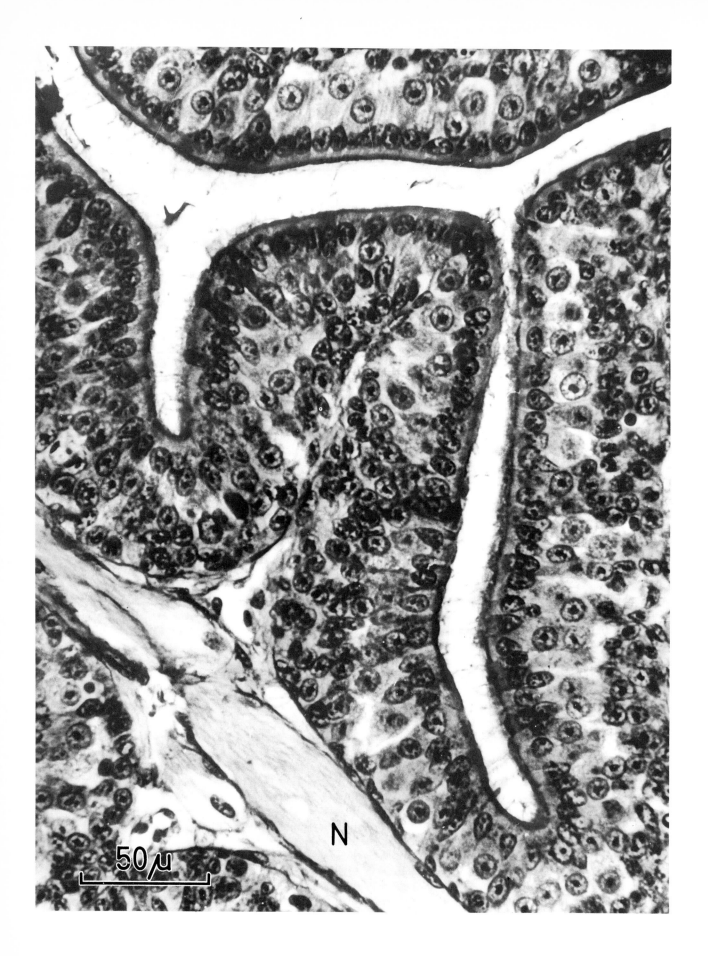

50μ

N

How the Salmon Migrates

Many species of fish undertake extensive migrations in the course of their life, often covering hundreds or thousands of miles. These are particularly impressive when the fish concerned, for instance many strains of salmon, return after a long absence to spawn in the very place where they themselves hatched out. The great distances covered in these migrations and the accuracy with which the place of birth is found again remind us of bird migrations. And the same question arises–what mechanism governs these fishes' ability to find their way back to their original home?

One's first thought is that it is a case of orientation by sight, of navigation by the sun or the stars. And it has, in fact, been proved that fishes do this. But the ability of salmon to make their way back to their first home depends a great deal on the sensitiveness of their noses.

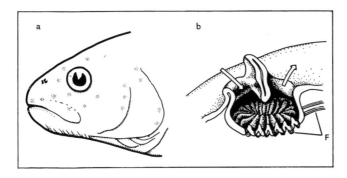

Figure 1. (a) Position of the nose opening in the head of a salmon trout (Salmo trutta).
(b) The rosette-like olfactory folds in the nose of a bony fish. F – olfactory fibres leading away from the nose. The arrow shows the direction in which the water flows.

Just like creatures who live on land, creatures which live in the water possess noses with which they detect odours that have dissolved in the water. In fishes the two nasal cavities are some distance apart in front of the eyes on top of the head. But, unlike the higher vertebrates, they are not connected with the mouth cavity. We find only one channel, which is covered by a fold of skin. And so fish have in effect a pipe which lies just under the skin and which can conduct the water in front. The bottom of this pipe is lined with mucous membrane and its surface area is greatly enlarged

Figure 2. Microphotograph of folded olfactory epithelium in the nose of a black-mouthed dogfish (Galeus melanostomus). N: nerve fibres leading from the olfactory cells (× 700).

by being packed into folds (Figs. 1b and 2, cf. p. 43). These folds are parallel to one another in the shape of a round or oval rosette. Most of the sensory cells are situated at the sides of the folds or in the hollows between. Bunched together under the folds are the fine nerve fibres which lead from the olfactory cells.

Thanks to the work of Professor Hasler and his colleagues we possess a great deal of information about the American salmon of the genus *Oncorhyncus*. The fish spawn in the upper reaches of the rivers. The young fish hatch out and grow up in the same place; they then migrate downstream and enter the sea. After three or four years they return to the rivers (Fig. 3). They by-pass, without deviating, the mouths of all the rivers they meet before reaching their own river, where they swim upstream until they come to the place where they grew up. There, in their turn, they spawn.

A simple experiment showed that this knowledge of a native river is not inherited. Old fish which were spawning were transferred to a neighbouring river and the young were allowed to grow up there: then, before migrating to the sea, these were taken back to the place where the parent fish were caught. Later, at the end of their time in the sea, the young returned to the river in which they had grown up. The decisive importance of the nose in all this can be proved by another experiment. If the noses of migrating salmon are plugged they lose their way, break up and scatter in a completely haphazard fashion among the various near-by rivers.

This clearly indicates the nature of the essential mechanism. During an especially sensitive period the fish become 'impregnated' with the smell of their native river, that is with the mixture of odorous substances which are peculiar to their haunts and which come from the water plants and the other forms of life and which naturally also depend on the particular conditions of the river bed. This mixture of odours is the information which is encoded by the sensory cells in the nose and conveyed in a complex pattern of impulses to specific centres in the brain. On the return migration the fish can once more recognize their original haunts by comparing these 'memory' odours with fresh ones.

In addition, however, there is a wide range of further signals which govern the behaviour of the salmon. For a great number of animals the thousands of migrating salmon represent a rich source of food: sea lions, bears–not to mention man–are enthusiastic salmon fishers. If, however, an enemy pollutes the water with the smell of its body the migration immediately halts. Even small concentrations of such a smell are enough to alarm the migrating salmon. Again, any mixture of unusual odours acts as a signal. One of the effective elements has been successfully isolated, an amino acid, L-serine. These discoveries make it clear that the migration of salmon as an activity governed by a sense of smell is no rigidly mechanical affair. They show that the responses can be adapted to the actual circumstances prevailing at the time by taking into account other information which also comes through the nose.

But the salmon cannot rely exclusively on their noses while they are migrating. Other sense organs come into play and it is unlikely that the salmon find the coast by their sense of smell alone. It is assumed that navigation by the sun–in which the sun's changing position would have to be calculated correctly–is the principal factor in trans-oceanic migration.

The salmon's great sensitivity to mechanical stimuli finally comes to their aid in the rivers. In a head of water with a certain concentration of odours they are probably not capable of moving to areas of greater concentration by their sense of smell alone. Their entry into a river which they recognize as their own by its smell is more likely to be the result of their orientation in respect to the current in the rush of water.

And so the nose of a fish is a receptor for odour signals from the environment and, acting in conjunction with many other sense organs and the centres of the nervous system which store and coordinate information, an organ which decisively determines such complex undertakings as these vast migrations.

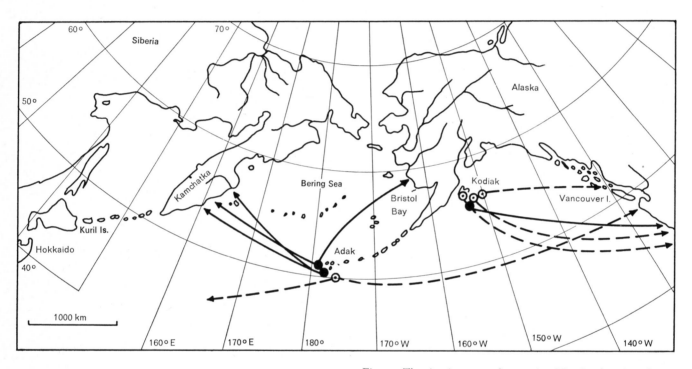

Figure 3. The migration courses of two species of Pacific salmon from their sea territory to the estuaries of their home rivers to which they return for spawning. Black circles and black lines, silver salmon (Oncorhyncus kisutch): open circles and broken lines, rainbow trout (Salmo gairdnerii).

Colour Photograph. Migrating Pacific salmon.

The Compass and the 'Internal Clock' of Migrant Birds

Every autumn millions of birds fly to their winter quarters, often thousands of miles from their native land, and in the following spring they return to their breeding grounds. This world-wide phenomenon raises the question of how birds find their way. Early observations and experiments showed that this achievement is at least partly due to the ability of birds to choose and maintain a direction independently of topographical landmarks. Young birds which were caught during the migration or shortly after setting off and were released after they had been taken elsewhere, flew parallel to their original course and in exactly the same direction as their undisturbed fellows. The question as to the sort of 'compass' the birds use was for a long time a matter of speculation, since the great distances covered by the birds seemed to make experimental control of their physical environment impossible. It was 1949 before these difficulties of method were overcome by the German zoologist Gustav Kramer. He observed that even in their cages captured starlings *(Sturnus vulgaris)* displayed a kind of migration behaviour. With birds kept in the open this urge took a definite direction. They strove to fly in much the same direction as the free migrants. This gave rise to experiments under controlled conditions. Early experiments, in which the earth's magnetic or electrical field was changed locally, had no effect on the direction which the birds took. Further investigation showed that the starlings used the sun for setting their course. When the sky was clear they always succeeded in taking the right direction; if a mirror was used to deflect the sun's rays, their course deviated to a predictable extent; if the sky was overcast they were bewildered and lost their ability to orientate (Fig. 2).

During the day the sun changes its position in the sky. In our hemisphere it travels from east to west via the south. Nevertheless, at all times of the day, the starlings tried to fly in the same direction. They must, therefore, have been able to make appropriate allowance for the time of day. This ability became particularly evident during experiments with an 'artificial' sun. A spotlight was fixed in an inside room, a starling was put in a tent and through its walls could see the light, which was cut down by a diaphragm to the angular diameter of the sun (which is 30 angular minutes). To the human observer inside the tent it was rather like being out of doors on a dull day, when the sun looks like a bright disc seen through a misty haze. In these conditions the birds flew at the same angle to the light as they would have to the sun at the corresponding time of day in order to keep on the migration course. They obviously allowed for a movement of the 'sun' which did not in fact take place. Similar orientation methods have since been discovered not only in many other species of birds but also in other types of animal life, for example crabs, many kinds of insects, fish and reptiles.

How do these birds know the time of the day? Further experiments showed that this knowledge is derived not so much from external factors as from a built-in time-keeping

Figure 2. Proof of orientation by the sun in the case of a caged starling. The bird can see the sky through six windows. When the sky is clear and the sun visible (a), the bird tries to fly in a definite direction; but when the sky is overcast (b) it shows no preference for any particular direction. If the fall of the light is changed by placing mirrors in front of the windows (c) and (d), the course the bird tries to take deviates predictably from its original direction. The horizontal circle is divided into eight sectors; the more marks that are registered, *the stronger the creature's attempt to fly in this direction (1 mark = 10 seconds migratory activity). The black arrows show the average direction; the dotted arrows show the direction in which the light falls. Other experiments gave further proof that the sun is used for orientation. Under an 'artificial sun' – a projector shining from an inner room – the birds always flew at the same angle to it as they would have flown to the real sun at the corresponding time of day.*

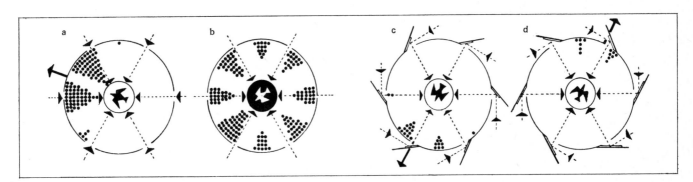

Figure 1. Cranes (Grus grus).

mechanism, an 'internal clock'. This clock is normally synchronized with the revolution of the earth by the natural, alternating cycle of day and night and adjusted to local time. By altering the time of the changeover from day to night with the aid of an artificial rhythm of light in a room cut off from proper daylight, the clock can be retimed and the direction in which the bird tries to fly arbitrarily be changed (Fig. 3). The outcome of such experiments might, at first, lead one to assume that the inner clock works on the principle of the hour glass–i. e., that some definite event, such as the dawn or the appearance of light in the artificial light cycle, starts up a timing process which then continues for a definite period. Further investigation, however, showed that the 'internal clock' operates on the principle of a self-sustained oscillation. It can be made to synchronize with external happenings, but it goes on functioning even without any external stimuli. Then, of course, the birds' clock usually shows a measurable variation from the frequency with which it has been synchronized, which is approximately one revolution per day. Variations of this sort occur in all clocks and one naturally expects to find them in a biological clock as well. As the birds normally live under conditions in which day and night follow one another such errors are always corrected.

Our knowledge of biological clocks does not come only from animals which find their way by using the sun as a compass. Many of us know this from personal experience. If we are in the habit of getting up at a definite time every day, we also frequently wake up at the same time when we do not need to, for instance on Sunday or on holiday. The latter example shows that it is not really a matter of reacting to sounds we hear subconsciously, such as the clatter of milk cans or the noise of traffic. We must, therefore, gain our knowledge from an 'internal clock' of which we are normally unaware. Similar experiments under strictly controlled conditions have been carried out with number of animals. These proved also that animals can be trained to react to definite times of the day. On the other hand, attempts to make them adjust themselves to cycles greatly different from the normal one of 24 hours were a failure. At the same time we know that many bodily functions have a rhythm of their own. For example, everyone probably knows about the rise and fall in our body temperature. It had once been assumed that a daily rhythm of this sort is a direct response to some

external rhythm, but we now know that it is governed by an 'internal clock'. Biological clocks of this sort are not confined to man and the higher animals; they are also found in plants and even in single cells.

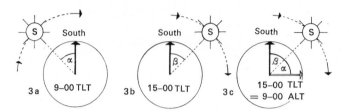

Figure 3. Diagram showing the direction chosen by a bird before, (a and b), and after (c), the internal clock has been re-timed. The bird wants to fly south. To do this it must fly at an angle of α° to the right of the sun at 0900 hrs TLT (true local time), at an angle of β° to the left of the sun at 1500 hrs. If the bird is kept in an artificial cycle of alternating light and darkness which is 6 hours later than the natural change from day to night its clock is adjusted accordingly. At 1500 hrs the physiological clock is only 0900 hrs ALT (artificial local time). Consequently the bird flies at an angle of α° to the right of the sun (S); that is, it flies west instead of south. The black arrow shows the bird's direction when its physiological clock is synchronized with local time; the white arrow shows its direction after the physiological clock has been adjusted.

The use of the sun as a compass can explain how migrant birds succeed in finding their way by day. Many species, however, migrate mainly or exclusively at night. Using Kramer's method, Mr. and Mrs. Sauer were able to prove that birds can pick up a direction at night with the aid of the fixed stars. Even under the artificial sky of a planetarium the birds knew their true migration course. In this case constellations probably provide the stimulus. The homing ability of carrier pigeons, however, still presents a special problem. They and a number of other birds can fly straight back home over great stretches of unfamiliar country even after they have been taken to strange, far-away places. This is a much greater achievement than just finding a direction. This was also thought to be a case of navigation by the stars and by the sun. The demands made on the efficiency of the sense organs involved and also the precision of the hypothetical internal clock are, however, incomparably higher than in a simple case of orientation, and it seems to be doubtful whether the birds fulfil these requirements. While some discoveries and observations support the idea that homing birds use a system of astronomical navigation, other facts do not fit in with such a theory. A final explanation of the problem has yet to be found.

Colour Photograph. Carrier pigeons (Columba livia domestica).

The Language of Bees

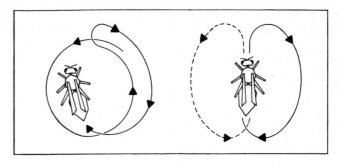

Figure 2. Worker bees which have discovered a source of nectar alert other bees in the hive by dancing. When the supply is near the news is given by the circular dance (left); where it is distant the news is given by the 'waggle dance' (right).

Human language is undoubtedly the most highly developed means of communication. But the languages of animals are also sometimes amazingly efficient. Like every language they consist of signs which can be perceived by the senses and which reveal a state or an intention of the sender, influence the receiver and give some information about certain matters and things. The signs can be seen, heard, touched or smelled. They are almost always symbols in code. The information they contain becomes comprehensible to the receiver after decoding. Only the person who knows the code of a piece of information can understand it. From the history of the deciphering of hieroglyphics and cuneiform inscriptions we know how difficult it is to break unknown codes. It is equally, if not even more difficult to penetrate the secrets of animals' language. Of these the one which has been most thoroughly studied is the amazingly efficient language of the honey bee.

A bee that has discovered an abundant supply of nectar makes tireless sorties to exploit its find. Every time it sheds its load of pollen or nectar in the hive, it informs other hive bees that there is something to be gathered and summons them to fly out as well and help bring it in. It does this by a recruiting dance. If the supply is less than 50 metres from the hive the bee runs round on the vertical honeycomb in small circles, going alternately to the left and to the right (Fig. 2). Other bees become interested and join in. In this way they learn that there is a supply of food near the hive which is worth exploiting. In addition they are informed of the scent of the flowers whose nectar or pollen was the reason for the dance. The dancer brings it into the hive in its fur and, in the intimacy of the dance, it is smelled by the bees following behind. Flower scents cling especially well to the bee's body–better, in fact, than to anything else that has been investigated. Finally, the bee just behind the dancer also learns about the actual value of the find–the richer this is the more spirited the dance and the longer it goes on. And so we can say that this bee-dancing fits naturally into our definition of language. It consists of signs which can be perceived by the senses, gives information about something which has been experienced by the person bringing the news, contains an appeal and several other pieces of information. The dance says in effect: "Fly out and search in the vicinity of the hive for flowers which smell like the dancer. When you find them, gather the nectar or the pollen."

The way this message is given is rational enough for short distances, but not for greater ones. Anyone who has to find a distant goal must know the direction in which it lies and how far it is away. The site of a supply of food which is more than fifty metres from the hive is communicated by the so-called 'waggle dance' (Fig. 2). In this dance the bees move quickly in semi-circular loops which are interrupted by straight runs during which the hind part of the body is waggled rapidly from side to side. The straight run–in which the bee does the tail wagging–always brings the bee back to the starting point of the previous loop. Semi-circle to the left–waggle run–semi-circle to the right–waggle run–etc. succeed one another. In this case, too, other bees follow the dancer. The number of complete dance figures (waggle run–semi-circle) which are performed in a definite time informs the bees which run behind the dancer how far away the source of food is. The further it is, the slower the dance (Fig. 3). If, for instance, it is 100 metres from the hive, 38 waggle runs are made per minute; if the distance is 500 metres, the number is 24, for 1000 metres it is 16 and for 5000 metres only 6. The distance to the supply is therefore translated into a definite number of dance figures per time unit. The exactness with which the bees follow the dance rhythms representing the actual flying distances and the accuracy with which they search at the right distance is altogether astonishing. A superlatively developed sense of time enables them to do this.

Not only is the distance communicated but also the direction in which they must fly–actually by the direction of the waggle run. How is this possible? How can the course to an unseen goal in the horizontal plane be indicated on the vertical honeycomb in the dark hive? A bee which flies in a straight line from the hive to the food supply maintains a definite angle to the sun (Fig. 4). If we assume that a bee

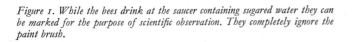

Figure 1. While the bees drink at the saucer containing sugared water they can be marked for the purpose of scientific observation. They completely ignore the paint brush.

flies to a supply of nectar in the south east at noon–the sun is then in the south–the angle between the direction of the bee's flight and the direction of the sun on its right is 45°. In this case, therefore, the flight course to the supply is 45° to the left of the sun. This angle–called the solar angle–is reproduced by the bee when it returns and does the straight waggle run inside the hive. This run represents the side of the solar angle pointing to the supply. The second side of this angle, i.e. the direction in which the sun lies, is shown by another orientation method available in this particular context, namely by the vertical direction which can be established with the organs of equilibrium. The solar angle, which now becomes the dance angle, is placed against this line. The direction in which the supply lies relative to the position of the sun is therefore converted into an angle corresponding to gravity. As, naturally, the site of a definite supply of nectar does not alter, whereas the position of the sun moving across the sky changes as time goes by, the solar angle is always growing bigger or smaller. In the same way bees which fly to one feeding ground for several hours constantly change the angle of their dance. But they do not need to keep flying to and fro between the hive and the supply. This is proved by the existence of the 'permanent dancers'. These, however, are mostly not worker bees but scouts who have already found a new nesting place for the swarm which will soon abandon the hive. There is no need for them to keep flying to the new home for there is nothing to fetch, whereas it is necessary to show as many of their companions as possible where this is so that the changeover can take place smoothly. And so they go on dancing for hours–with small breaks, of course–without leaving the hive. As time passes they change the angle of their dance in an astonishing way, to make it coincide with the change in the angle between the nesting place and the position of the sun outside. They are able to correct the solar angle to allow for the passage of time, an ability which also plays an important part in orientation. Like birds and many other animals bees are capable of using the sun as a compass.

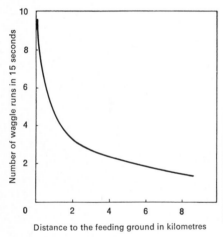

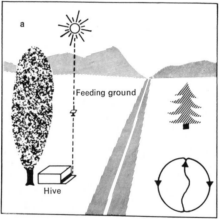

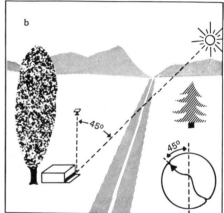

Figure 3. The curve makes clear the correlation between the distance of the supply from the hive and the tempo in the waggle dance. Horizontal axis, distance in kilometres; vertical axis, number of waggle dances in a quarter of a minute.

Figure 4. Even the direction of the food supply is communicated in the waggle dance, in which reference is made to the position of the sun. If a bee has flown to the south at noon it runs straight up the vertical honeycomb on its return, performing its waggle dance. At 3 o'clock in the afternoon the feeding ground is 45° to the left of the sun, which has meanwhile moved south-west, and the waggle run now points 45° to the left of the perpendicular.

Colour Photograph. Honey bee (Apis mellifica) at the flower of a rudbekia (Rudbeckia).

What Signals will Catch a Male?

One of the features of life is its transitoriness. If life is to continue, animals and plants must produce new individuals before they die. With many living things reproduction occurs non-sexually by division, breaking into bud or by the formation of bulbs. But sexual reproduction is more frequent. Excitingly, most living things are of two types of nature–of male or female sex. Both sexes produce germ cells. Apart from relatively few exceptions, new individuals come into being only when a germ cell of one sex unites with a germ cell of the opposite sex. Each egg must be fertilized by a sperm cell. The characteristics of the parent animals are then transmitted to the offspring by the information stored in the chromosomes. The devices that nature has contrived in order to ensure the fertilization which will maintain the species are far more varied and more numerous than our imagination can even visualize.

In most cases fertilization cannot occur unless both sexes meet. To ensure that this also takes place at the right time among animals which live alone nature takes special precautions. But it is not just a question of meeting. The future couple–at least in those cases where a meeting is to lead to mating–must also recognize one another. To us the ability to recognize fellow human beings is something which is natural and self-evident. For one thing we grow up among them. But most creatures reach maturity without ever having seen one of their own species before. They cannot learn what their future partner looks like; the knowledge of this 'image' must be inborn.

This inborn 'picture' of partners could–at least in theory–be detailed and comprehensive. In fact, however, only abstractions, surprisingly simplified models of the actual appearance are handed down from generation to generation. Nevertheless these allow the opposite sex to be recognized reasonably easily, as they are so constituted that in the normal habitat of the species they are sent out only, or almost only, by the partner. The perception of the model, like that of the partner, results in definite behaviour patterns or, in other words, the stimuli emanating from the model, like a key, unlock the door to definite and significant responses. We speak, therefore, of key stimuli.

Where butterflies are concerned one is inclined to ascribe particular significance to the often beautiful colouring and marking. But here, too, the truth is that the features by which a male butterfly bent on sexual display recognizes his partner are very simple. He does not need to remember all the details of the shape in which she appears. A few outstanding ones are all the signals that are necessary.

The naturalist is especially interested in the precise structure of these signals and key stimuli. One of the subjects used for studying such problems is the fritillary *(Argynnis paphia)*. This magnificent butterfly is frequently to be seen in July and August flying near the edges of woods and in glades (Colour photograph and Fig. 1). It lives on the nectar from the flowers of thistles, blackberries and elders. In fine weather the males become eager to find a mate and they embark on flights which are quite different in character from the flights they make in search of food. As soon as a male discovers a female, he flies to her. By means of cleverly devised experiments with decoys it was possible to discover the signal stimuli which inspire these courtship flights. What is surprising is that the shape of the objective is of no real importance. Circular discs, squares, triangles, even elongated rectangles which have surfaces similar to those of a female interest the male just as much as a true-to-life copy (Fig. 2). A similar thing can be observed in the case of flights made to decoys which are of the same shape but of different sizes. All the paper butterflies shown in Fig. 3 were approached, although this happened more frequently with the larger than with the small ones. This statement also holds good for the decoys which were twice or four times the size of a natural female fritillary. There are, therefore, key stimuli which are more effective than the natural ones.

Figure 2. Female decoys used in the experiments with the fritillary. The shape is unimportant; all the figures with a surface similar to that of the butterfly were approached just as frequently.

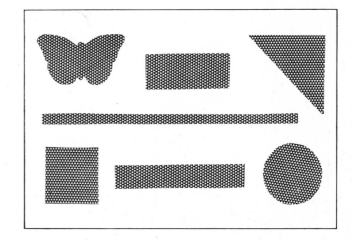

Figure 1. Male fritillaries at the inflorescene of a buddleia (Buddleia variabilis). By the right hand butterfly can be seen the long proboscis, bent in the shape of a V, with which the creatures can suck up the nectar secreted deep within the flower tubes.

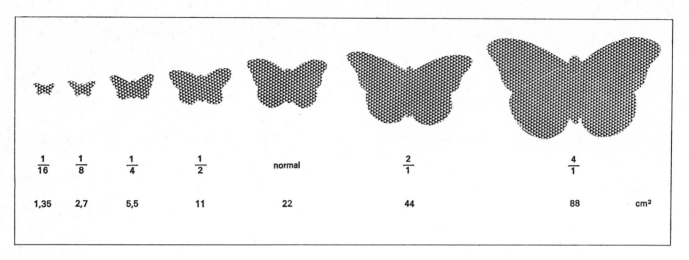

$\frac{1}{16}$	$\frac{1}{8}$	$\frac{1}{4}$	$\frac{1}{2}$	normal	$\frac{2}{1}$	$\frac{4}{1}$	
1,35	2,7	5,5	11	22	44	88	cm²

Figure 3. Even the size of the decoy paper butterflies is of only minor importance. All of them were approached just as though they were genuine females. However, the number and intensity of the approach flights increases with an in- *crease in the size of the decoys. Those which are oversized exert a more powerful attraction than genuine females. They work as a supernormal stimulus. (Normal wingspan = 60 mm.)*

These are called supernormal stimuli. Size is, therefore, of some importance, but a very minor one. The colour of the decoy and its way of moving were far more important. It must be of a similar yellow to the fritillary and be visible and invisible alternately, like the fluttering of the wings of the female which is being pursued. The way in which this is done in the experiment is immaterial. It made no difference whether the effect was produced by the wing beat of an artificial butterfly whose wing was painted brownish yellow on top and black underneath or by revolving a similarly painted paper butterfly on its axis. In most of the experiments cylinders were used which were painted half black and half fritillary yellow and these were rotated round their long axis. (Striped cylinder decoy, Fig. 4).

In spite of the poverty of distinguishing marks and the abstract nature of the optical movement signals, a male fritillary will not fly very often to a false objective in its familiar habitat. But it does occasionaly happen. Members of the same sex and immature females especially inspire courting flights. But nature sees to it that a fritillary on the look-out for a wife is not kept too long in error. As a further signal only females ready to mate give off a certain odour and they alone perform a special kind of whirring flight at the approach of the male. If the object which the male is approaching behaves differently his interest rapidly cools. But if the first response occurs the approach and mutual recognition is followed by an extensive courtship which finally culminates in mating.

Figure 4. A cylinder of which one half is painted yellow and the other half black and which rotates sufficiently fast round its longer axis sends out the signals which signify 'female' to a male fritillary.

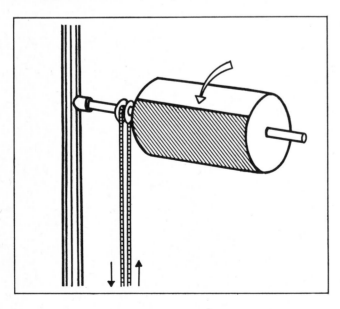

Colour Photograph. Fritillary (Argynnis paphia) on a dwarf elder (Sambucus ebulus).

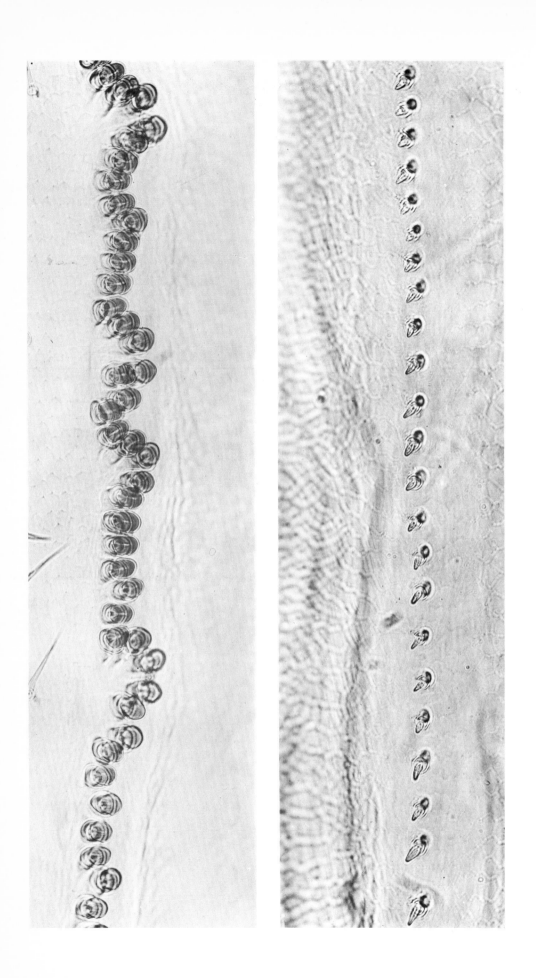

Grasshoppers' Songs

As with birds, it is mostly only the male crickets and grass-hoppers which sing; and each species sings its own song, which it knows by instinct and does not need to learn. But how do crickets and grasshoppers sing? If one considers the number of groups of these little singers which exist, especially in hot countries, one is amazed at the astonishing variety of types of musical apparatus that one finds. About two dozen different ones have been described. In most cases these are organs which produce a strident noise. A comb-like structure and a sharp edge are rubbed against one another. When the short-horned field crickets sing the back legs are often moved up and down simultaneously. A row of little teeth on the inside of the leg (Fig. 1) is scraped against a raised vein in the fore-wing. It is one of nature's little jokes that the mirror image of this apparatus is to be found in some other grasshoppers–rows of little teeth on a protruding wing vein (though it is often a different vein) and an edge on the inside of the hind leg. Crickets and long-horned tree grasshoppers make their song in a different way, by rubbing their fore-wings together. When they do this a comb-like ridge on the underside of the top wing (in crickets it is usually the right one), in tree grasshoppers it is usually the left one) is scraped by a sharp edge of the lower wing.

But these two main methods by no means exhaust the range of possibilities. During flight the grasshopper *Psophus* makes a rattling sound with its bright red hind wings which move like a pair of fans. Many field grasshoppers normally make their songs by grinding their teeth–the sounds being produced when their two upper jaws are rubbed together. The grasshopper *Mecostethus* lives in very wet fields; it sings by shooting its hind legs violently backwards, so that its spurs grate over the veins of its wing, making a crackling noise. This strange singing movement is a defensive action which is repeated rhythmically and is audible.

The results of the very precise coordination in the working of the muscles which activate the sound apparatus–in the male field cricket there are always 14 pairs of muscles situated in the middle of the breast–are hardly pure notes: they are usually sounds ranging over a fairly wide frequency band and certain frequency groups can be stressed–in the field cricket, for example, this is in the region of 4,000 to 5,000 cycles per second. But quite a number of grasshopper species send out frequencies which extend into the ultra-sonic range–in the case of the large green grasshopper (*Tettigonia viridissima*) it is as much as 100,000 cycles per second.

Can another member of the species for whom this is intend-ed hear it at all? With crickets and tree grasshoppers the main organs of hearing, the tympanal organs which are equipped with a drum membrane as a sound receiver, are situated in the tibia of the fore-legs; but in field grasshop-pers they are on the first abdominal segment. They are in some ways more and in some ways less effective than the human ear–less in so far as crickets and grasshoppers obviously lack the ability, so familiar in man, of distinguish-ing between tones of different frequencies; more in so far as at least a few species respond to frequencies that are well inside the ultrasonic band. But if these hearing organs are unable to distinguish between frequencies, what makes them efficient as receptors and transformers of information in cooperation with the central nervous system? There are two things. Firstly, their ability to locate a source of sound. If the body is turned obliquely to this sound the hearing organ which is turned towards it is stimulated more strongly than the one which is turned away and after calculating the difference the central nervous system sends impulses to the leg muscles. The insect places itself symmetrically to the source of the sound and, attracted and guided by its part-ner's song, hunts down the source. Secondly it is very probable that its hearing organs are able to catch the rhythmical time pattern characteristic of the song of a species and to pass this information to the central nervous system. But the important thing is that the song which is intended for another member of the same species, particu-larly a female, is correctly 'understood' by that member–an ability which is also inborn. The song has a stimulating or attracting effect, but the response is only to the song of a member of the same species singing in the neighbourhood at the same time. The unmistakable difference between the songs is especially striking and effective in the case of relat-ed species living near one another in the same area (Fig. 2). Mis-mating is a very rare occurence; the two creatures simply no longer 'understand' one another. Sometimes, however, the songs of related species are so alike that a confusion of sexual partner could occur: but the species concerned usually prefer to live in such different habitats that they hardly ever meet.

The male's song is certainly intended primarily, as we have said, for the female. But the males also hear and understand one another. With the little ones which are not confined to any definite locality this can result in many males congregat-ing in a relatively small area and singing almost in chorus.

Figure 1. Section of the stridulation ridge on the inside of the hind femur of a field grasshopper (Gomphocerippus rufus); left, of the male; right, of the female.

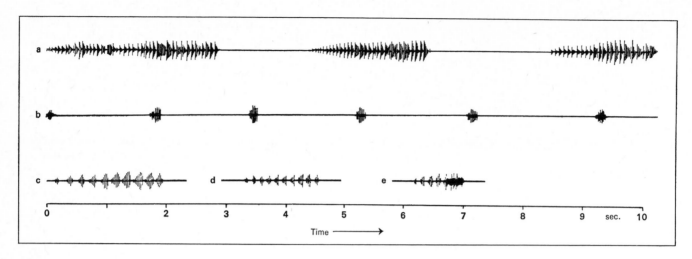

Figure 2. Songs of five field grasshoppers of the Chorthippus order. (a) Ch. biguttulus, (b) Ch. brunneus; both species are closely related, live near one another and sing very different songs. (c) Ch. montanus, (d) Ch. longicornis, (e) Ch. dorsatus. The close relationship of the last three species is reflected in a certain similarity of song. (c) lives in very wet, (e) in moderately wet, (d) in fairly dry areas.

In this way they probably exert a more powerful attraction on the females. On the other hand male tree grasshoppers and crickets, which are more or less confined to one spot–each male cricket, in fact, inhabits its own burrow in the ground–the singing may have the effect of scattering the other males with the result that these are to some extent distributed equally over the area.

But the importance of the songs as a medium of information is further complicated by the fact that the males can sing several kinds of song. It is often possible to distinguish clearly three main songs–especially in the field grasshoppers –and these songs can certainly be run into one another by linking passages reflecting the mood of the singer. A male which is relatively isolated from others of the same species (that is, none of these singing in the immediate vicinity) sings the 'usual' or 'calling song' which has the effect of attracting a female which is in a suitable mood. Two males which meet sing the shorter 'rival's song', the beginning of which is not infrequently strongly accentuated. In the presence of the female, however, especially if she is unresponsive, it changes to the 'courting song' which sometimes continues for a long time. The song usually ends with an attempt at mating, which is often vain but is usually continued as long as the female does not take to flight.

The significance of the 'rival's song' which fails to attract the female varies with different species and groups of species. With the field crickets it is a phenomenon which accompanies the often bitter combat between two males; with many field grasshoppers, whose males are less choosy and make advances to anything that looks at all like a grasshopper, it can be a help to sexual recognition. A male comes upon another male by mistake; the latter responds with the

'rival's song', the first one is put in the picture and both move away. The significance of the courting song, however, must be sought in the harmonizing of the mood of the two sexual partners. Indeed, quite often the efforts of a male grasshopper go unrewarded, even though it keeps on singing its courting song, for the female is inclined to 'listen to' the male only at certain periods in the maturing of the egg in the ovaries.

During the peak phases of the female's readiness to mate, particularly before the first actual copulation, and often, too, after the eggs have been laid, the whole proceeding can be curtailed. In the case of many field grasshoppers the female which is ready to mate answers the courting male: their songs are alike, but the female's is usually quieter and its rhythm less strict. But the effect on the male is quite astonishing. He becomes extremely active, rushes about, orientates himself to the female, sings more passionately and leaps in the direction of the partner which is exchanging songs with him. The female may also move towards the male and they quickly meet and mate. Thus this song proves to have an especially striking significance. It is specific to the species, it is correctly understood by another member of the species, it expresses a definite, mutual mood, it produces action, it facilitates orientation to the partner and it ensures that mating will be speedy.

Colour Photograph. Short-winged green grasshopper (Euthystira brachyptera).

How is a Signal Flag Rolled Up?

Many animals have conspicuous coloured markings on certain parts of the body. These are signals which have a definite meaning for members of the same species and sometimes also for other species. The clearer such a signal, the more effective it is. There are, however, good reasons why such signals should be displayed only occasionally rather than all the time. One reason is that definite signals and the message which they convey are necessary only in certain situations. Another is that a feature which is too conspicuous makes an animal an easy prey to its enemies. In the struggle for existence, therefore, it is better to be inconspicuous and well camouflaged and to display the signal only at the right time. Our three-spined stickleback *(Gasterosteus aculeatus)* is a good example of this. Normally the males are of a nondescript, greyish brown colour. In the spring, at mating time, the male stickleback becomes a brilliant creature with an emerald green back and a bright red belly. This is a sign that it wants to mate. The red belly is a double signal. It warns any rival entering its territory to expect to be attacked. On the other hand, the same signal inspires the appropriate response in a female which is ready to mate. The change in colour occurs once in the year and is purely seasonal. Other creatures such as the sea-horse *(Hippocampus guttulatus)* can, however, change colour at any time and within a matter of seconds. There are various ways of producing a sudden change of this sort. Frequently the striking features are to be found on parts of the body which can be concealed or folded up. The signal flag can be unfurled, so

Figure 1. Pigment cell of a vertebrate. Left, the pigment is concentrated into a ball in the centre of the cell. Right, the pigment has spread to all the branches of the cell, thus occupying a larger area and determining the animal's colour.

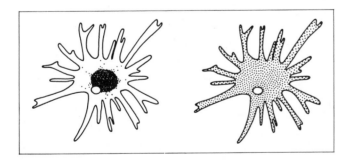

Figure 3. A school of unicorn fish (Naso thymnoides). Top, normal colouring. Bottom, some males have changed colour and now have small, vivid, narrow, light blue stripes.

Figure 2. Pigment cells of a cuttlefish. If the ray-like muscle cells go slack, the cell becomes spherical and does not take up much space (left). If the muscles contract (right) the pigment cell becomes flat and covers a larger area.

to speak, by spreading or extending the bodily appendages. Many fishes use the dorsal fins for this purpose, while reptiles have inflatable throat sacs or collars.

Another method of changing colour is that used by sea-horses, sticklebacks and many other fishes, as well as by crayfish, cuttlefish, snails and starfish. It is called physiological colour change by the biologist. Thousands of closely packed pigment cells, or chromatophores, often exist in the skin of such creatures. The colour photograph shows an example of chromatophores in the skin of a river crayfish *(Astacus fluviatilis)*. In most cases several different types of pigment cell occur side by side, each one containing a distinct pigment. The range of colours extends from a whitish yellow through orange, red and brown to black. The chromatophores are highly branched cells, their pigment is a concentration of granules, which may lie either in a tight bunch in the centre of the cell (pigment aggregation) or be dispersed throughout the whole cell (pigment dispersion) (Fig. 1). The mechanisms which cause this dispersion or this concentration have not so far been explained. If the pigment is concentrated in one place these tiny specks have no appreciable effect on the coloration of the surfaces of the body. If it is dispersed, the pigment covers a considerable area of the skin and it then determines the body colour. Since the different types of chromatophores are mostly disposed independently of one another, the body colour can take on one shade or the other, or even an intermediate shade. A purely local arrangement of certain chromatophores or their deployment to some particular area makes a local change of colour possible, and therefore the sudden appearance of a brightly coloured spot. The chromatophores of cuttlefish are an exception to this very common type. These spherical cells are filled evenly with pigment. Several small muscle fibres project from them like rays. If these contract the cell goes flat and covers a larger area (Fig. 2).

The chromatophore condition is controlled either by blood-borne hormones (colour-change hormones) or by nerves, or finally by the two together. It can be proved that many animals' brains include centres responsible for supervising the whole system of colour change. As the possibility of changing colour is frequently used for the purpose of simulating the brightness and colour of the background, the colour change centres are often controlled by the eye. How complicated such a control system can be is shown by recent researches on the minnow *(Phoxinus laevis)*. In this case certain definite areas of the brain connected with colour change are themselves sensitive to light and are covered with chromatophores whose activity–unlike that of skin melanophores–is not governed by the eye. We have here, presumably, a complicated connection involving interaction between the pigment cells, the colour change centres, the eyes and the hormone glands.

In animals whose colour changes are purely seasonal, like the stickleback, the change takes place slowly. In other species it is a matter of seconds. Thus the unicorn fish *(Naso thymnoides)* swimming in the open waters of tropical seas is normally very drab. Within a few seconds of a male becoming interested in a female a bright blue, saddle-like patch appears across the front part of its back and light blue stripes show down its sides (Fig. 3). The Australian bearded lizard *(Amphibolurus barbatus)*, which is normally olive brown, suddenly displays a shining yellow with orange stripes if it is molested. The males of another agamid species, *Calotes versicolor*, (versicolor = changing colour) constantly change the colour of their throats, alternating between light and dark, when they are in combat. And when the fight is over, the victor displays a gleaming red throat, while the loser withdraws looking brownish grey. Finally, the chameleon has become proverbial for its ability to change colour. Although really very little is still known about the meaning of such signals, one gets the impression that it is a sort of sign language. Together with certain body positions– which might be described as gestures–colour change provides a sign language which living creatures can employ.

But it must be pointed out that this particular function of colour change is only one among several which are so far known to us. The others include adaptation to background –in the form of protective colouring–and to the varying strength of the sunlight.

Colour Photograph. Pigment cell in the skin of a river crayfish (Astacus fluviatilis), magnified about 400 times.

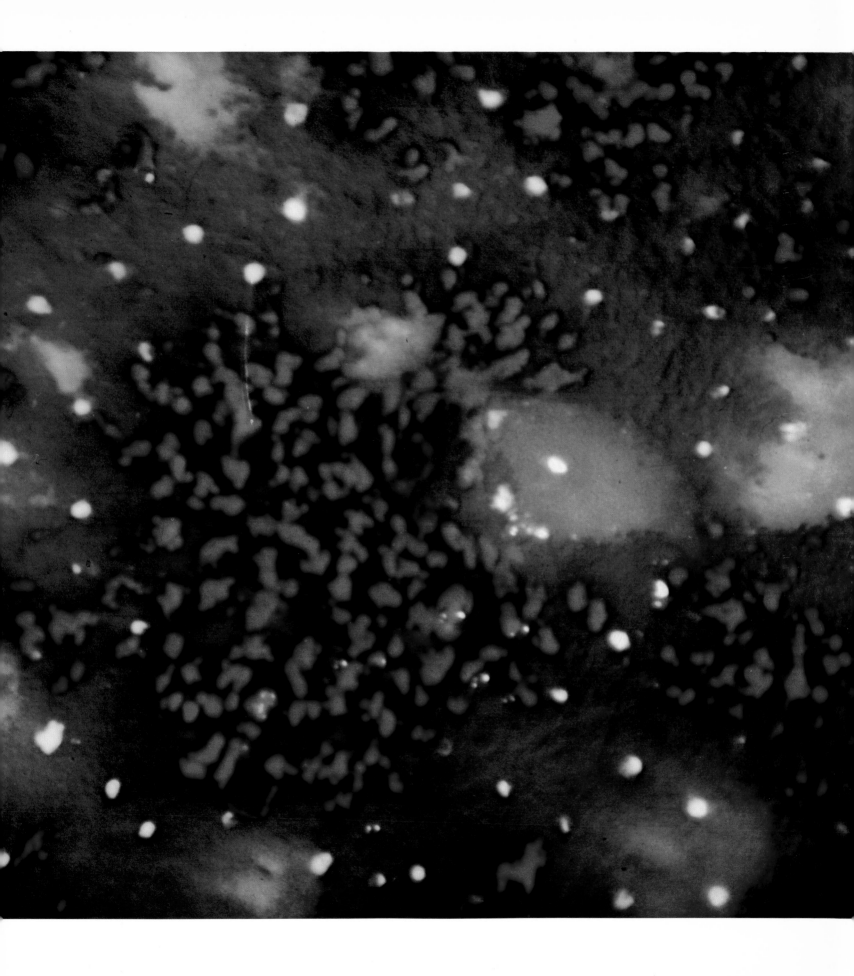

1

4

2

5

3

6

Colour Signals as a Dynamic Means of Demarcating Territory

When Charles Darwin became acquainted with the fairyland of the coral reefs during his voyage round the world in the *Beagle* he attempted to explain the origin of the atolls; yet he simply gave an amazed and delighted account of the variety of living creatures which he saw and never bothered about any 'Darwinian' explanation of their many and often bizarre individual forms. Neither Darwin nor anyone else who has visited a coral reef has advanced any even remotely acceptable theory to explain how the incredible splendour of colour which distinguishes many of its inhabitants, especially the fishes, originated and functions. The most varied speculations were advanced. According to one view the coral reef was brilliantly coloured so that the vivid colours of the fish could be a form of camouflage; others thought it was one of nature's extravagances and due to excessively favourable living conditions. For all extravagance of this sort, however, a simple explanation can usually, if not always, be found if one asks the following question and knows the animal species concerned: What is the function whose survival value produced the selection which has bred this improbable form of the species? The answer to this question in no way detracts from the beauty which appears in the animal world, be it the song of a bird or, as in the present case, the brilliant, magnificent colours of the coral fish. The well-known biologist and authority on animal behaviour, Konrad Lorenz, more Darwinian than Darwin himself, was the first to investigate this question in connection with the coral fish and he made the discovery that it is the struggle for existence which has produced these jewels among fish. To throw a clearer light on this lapidary statement I must digress a little.

Figure 1. Blue trigger fish (Odonus niger). An example of a peaceful and therefore inconspicuously marked inhabitant of the coral reef.

Figure 2. Picasso trigger fish (Rhinecanthus aculeatus). Brilliant and quarrelsome.

Figure 3. Dragon fish (Pterois volitans), slow and dangerous. It seizes its prey by driving it into a corner and flapping its pectoral fins like oyster baskets. A powerful venom, similar to a cobra's, protects it against enemies.

Figures 4–6. Butterfly fishes. (4) Chaetodon auriga, (5) Chaetodon vagabundus, (6) Chaetodon falcula. The three closely related species are almost the same shape but their markings are different. They specialize in eating corals, anemones and tube worms for food. They are aggressive only towards members of their own species with the same markings.

'The struggle for existence' is not waged mainly between predator and prey as is all too often assumed out of ignorance. The struggle between rivals which eat the same things– that is, their struggle for their daily food–is far more deadly. The first kind of struggle can, of course, also produce natural selection, as is shown by the combat which, since the earliest tertiary period, has been waged between the grasses in the plant world and the grass-eaters in the animal world. The former became increasingly tough because of silica stratification; the latter acquired an increasingly harder and more complex tooth enamel to master that. Why is this struggle not so dangerous? Because the eaters can never completely destroy the species being eaten since this eventually becomes too scarce to go on being the staple food. When the dingo came to Australia with man it exterminated not the marsupial species which became its food but the predatory marsupial competing with it and whose hunting methods were inferior to its own.

This kind of competitive struggle has bred an extreme specialization, particularly in the coral reef, as scarcely any other biotope in a very confined space offers so many different possibilities for existence – so-called 'ecological niches'. It is possible to get along and make a living as an 'average fish' if one takes a fancy to the free-swimming small live creatures. One can, however, also go in for cracking hard shell snails, gobbling up the heads of tube worms with lightning speed, or stealing prey already held in the venomous grip of the polyps. It is possible to become immune even to the numbing poison of the polyps and draw the tiny creatures from their chalk tubes. And if one has a powerful jaw one can crunch and eat even pieces of coral. One can evolve into a cleaner or destroyer of the vermin on the other fishes and literally pick the lice off them. Or–the craziest of all ways of life–swim up looking exactly like a cleaner and, in this guise, exploit the client's trust with the aim of using one's sharp teeth like a parasite to tear pieces out of its skin (cf. p. 119).

Such specialization in pursuit of a definite struggle for food only pays as long as things are so arranged that not more is eaten than can grow again. Therefore each of these fishes must guard its feeding ground and defend it against competitors. Naturally each of these specialists is only concerned that no member of its own species crosses its path as a specialist in the same food, just as a businessman dislikes it if another one starts up a similar business in the same street, but does not object to the presence of a different type of business next door. Each of these coral fishes specializing in some definite method of getting its food has to a certain extent its own professional dress. Almost all the fishes under discussion are faithful to their own locality; they display their full aggressiveness only at the centre of their territory and become more timid the nearer they venture to their boundaries. The colouring and marking which is specific to the species and therefore essential for acquiring food promptly warn any roving fish that may be approaching the territory of one of its own species, just as the marauder at the same time reveals its own presence from a distance and alerts the occupier of the territory. The distribution of colour among these fishes is different from what it is among fresh-water fishes which are just as beautifully coloured. There is no delicate pattern, no gradations or shades, no iridescent colours, nor the rapid change of colour which is such a startling reflection of the inner mood of tropical fresh-water fish. The colours here are extensive and lavish; not iridescent and shimmering but deep and rich, as in a poster designed to show up at a distance, which is why Konrad Lorenz pithily described these fishes as 'poster-coloured'. The colours do not change in accordance with a mood although the fish reveal an ability to change colour by adopting protective colouring at night. Nor is the brilliant coloration associated with breeding time, as it is in the case of fresh-water fish. Even the young fishes are quite vivid, often much more so than the adults of the same species. Signal apparatus which originated during the evolution of the species and which start a biologically significant behaviour response in other living creatures, mostly members of the same species, are usually described as releasers in the theory of behaviour. Lorenz thought it obvious to suspect that there would be releasers of this kind in these colours. The question asked at the beginning became more precise: What special behaviour patterns are likely to be released by the poster colours? The fishes very quickly provided an answer to this question. Even at the first attempts to keep coral fishes in the aquarium it became clear that it was quite impossible to keep several specimens together, especially if they belonged to the most brilliant species. Fierce fights broke out the moment they were put in and went on until the strongest fish ruled the tank. The others fled to near the surface and into the corners, their fins torn and mutilated, and their slightest movement drew fresh violence–showing a correlation between the fishes' brilliant coloration and their aggressiveness and ferocity. Species with plain, protective coloration were completely peaceful. The black angel fish *(Pomacanthus arcuatus)* occupies an interesting intermediate position. When young it is decidedly poster-coloured and correspondingly aggressive, but when sexually mature it is dark grey, has black spots on its scales and is completely peaceful.

All these fishes are normally peaceful towards different species when they are living under natural conditions. It is only when a fish in an aquarium finds no member of its own species but does find one of another species of rather similar colour that it is likely to become aggressive.

By observing the number of skirmishes and fights occuring in one of the tanks containing several brilliantly coloured fishes it is possible to establish the fact that marking and coloration are the cause of this aggression. The strong development of aggression within the species in connection with the territorial behaviour described above has an important biological significance. The effectiveness of the two behaviour patterns together in maintaining the species is caused by the fish being distributed as equally as possible over the existing living space. This ensures that the best possible use is made of the available food supply. The reason for the extremely brilliant and varied colour pattern of coral fishes is, therefore, to be sought for in the many possibilities for life, and particularly for getting food, in the same living area. By employing optical methods of intimidation the coral fishes are spared a constant and exhausting battle for feeding grounds.

Colour Photograph. The butterfly fish Chelmon rostratus, an example of a poster-coloured reef fish.

a

b

Friendly Signals between Fishes

In recent years all sorts of 'partnerships for mutual aid'– so-called symbioses–have been discovered among marine animals. Partnerships of this kind are charming subjects of study for the student of animal behaviour; they also give him an opportunity to investigate the methods which different species use in order to reach an understanding with each other. The cleaning symbioses of sea fish provide a splendid example of this, for with them understanding is achieved with the help of optical signals. We observed these cleaners for the first time in 1953 among the coral reefs of the Caribbean Sea. We were about twenty feet down, on the sea bed, watching the bright, hustling life of the tropical fish. Then a grouper *(Epinephelus)* swam up, slowly moving its torn breast fins. It made for a large block of coral, stopped above it and opened its huge mouth. Immediately two little blue neon gobies *(Elacatinus oceanops)* appeared on the scene. They searched to and fro along the predator's great body and one disappeared into its open mouth. I naturally thought that the grouper would swallow it, but nothing of the sort happened. The grouper kept perfectly still and when the other fish came near a gill cover it lifted this up and let the fish in. After a while the grouper suddenly snapped its mouth together, without completely closing it, and immediately opened it wide again. This was obviously a signal to the little fish, which swam out of the grouper's mouth. The other little fish was given a similar warning by a brief flick of the gill cover. Then the grouper shook itself several times and the two fishes returned to the block of coral from which they had come. Shortly after this an angel fish swam up and once again the little blue fishes began to work on it. Then came a lot more big fishes and the small ones were soon busy on all of these. We had quickly discovered that the small fishes removed parasites from the big ones and cleaned any injuries to their skin as well (Fig. 1). In the meantime we have discovered a whole number of cleaners. In the Indian Ocean the wrasse *Labroides dimidiatus* which appears in the colour photograph has made this its special job in life. Pairs of these fishes inhabit definite areas of coral reef which are regularly frequented by other reef fishes. Often a whole line of fishes can be seen queueing up for their turn. Cleaner and host

Figure 1a. A cleaner grooms the corner of the mouth of a surgeon fish (Acanthurus spec.).

Figure 1b. A wrasse (Plectorhynchus diagrammus) – at the top left of the photograph – holds its mouth open as an invitation to a tiny cleaner – above its eyes – to groom it.

understand one another by means of a whole series of movements, each of which conveys a definite meaning. The cleaner can summon a fish for cleaning by dancing up and down in front of it and wriggling its body all the time. This striking, see-saw way of swimming which functions as a signal probably originated in a conflict in which the fish was torn between a desire to swim towards or away from big fish. The fact that the cleaners dance in such an energetic and striking way in front of large fish and also in front of divers suggests that here is a case where even now the urge to approach and the urge to flee conflict with one another. If the cleaner knows its host very well it hardly dances at all. If it is searching the host it fans it continuously with its ventral fins. In this way the cleaner informs the host fish exactly where it is working and the host turns towards it, moving or lifting up the fins which the cleaner is nudging, or opening its mouth if the cleaner swims there. Again the fish being groomed can inform the cleaner when it wants it to finish and, in fact, it always does this in the same way–by pretending to close its mouth, flicking its gill covers and shaking its body. In addition it can invite the cleaner to come by adopting certain positions which have already been described.

The cleaners give their attention particularly to small irregularities on the skin of the host, such as bright spots and marks, and try to remove these. But mistakes can be made. For example we had in the aquarium a small porcupine fish which was carrying fine bits of skin on its spines. The cleaners wanted to remove them and it was only after they had got repeatedly pricked that they gave up.

The hosts recognize their cleaner not only by their behaviour but also by their very striking appearance. At first we had merely suspected this, because cleaners from different areas often look very much alike. This suspicion was confirmed in a very surprising way in the Maldives. We had repeatedly noticed that host fishes jerked away, even fled, from a 'cleaner'. I did not know what to make of this until, one day, I caught one of these 'cleaners' and saw to my great astonishment that I was holding not a cleaner but a small predator of the sabre-toothed blenniid group. I had already observed how relatives of these fishes set on other fishes and tore pieces out of their skin and their fins. The fish in my hand was doing the same thing. In order to approach its victim more easily it simulated the appearance and behaviour of a cleaner. In this way it deceived the hosts, which often awaited it with their mouths open and their gill covers up and fled only when it attacked them. The resemblance between a cleaner and its mimic is quite bewildering (Fig. 2). Both are blue and have a horizontal black stripe running the length of the body. The likeness is increased by the fact that the imitator dances just like the cleaner. The great importance of the cleaners in the life of the coral reef fishes was recently established by C. Limbaugh in a remarkable experiment. He removed all cleaners known to him from two reefs in the Bahamas. Thereupon a large majority of the reef fishes departed, leaving the reefs more or less deserted. Only a few faithfuls remained and at the end of two weeks these had all manner of skin and fin injuries, such as open wounds, sores and fungus growths. Eventually young cleaners came along, bringing with them new hosts. Meanwhile, cleaning symbiosis has been discovered in the Mediterranean, the Red Sea, the Indo-Pacific and in the tropical parts of the Atlantic. If conditions in the Indo-Pacific region are compared with those in the tropical parts of the Atlantic, it is astonishing to find that only a few species are active as cleaners in the former area. By far the commonest cleaner is the wrasse *(Labroides dimidiatus)*; in addition there are a few other cleaners of the same order. All these wrasses look very much alike. Their body is marked with a conspicuous longitudinal black stripe. This is true even of the shark-sucker *(Echeneis naucrates)* which 'does for' the sharks—its only title to a relationship with the cleaners. In the same way most cleaners of the Indo-Pacific carry a common trade sign.

In the tropical parts of the Atlantic (the Caribbean and Bermuda area), on the other hand, I observed seven different looking cleaners which belonged to different families of fish. Of these the neon goby *(Elacatinus oceanops)* and the wrasse *(Thalassoma bifasciatum)* have specialized most in cleaning. In any case the wrasses groom only when they are young, while the neon gobies perform this service throughout their lives. They even ventured into the mouths of predators. Both cleaners had a horizontal black line along the sides of their bodies; the neon goby was also deceptively like the cleaning wrasses of the Indo-Pacific region in its colouring. That suggests an interesting explanation.

The Indo-Pacific and the Atlantic are known to have been joined for most of the tertiary period. And so even today we find many common orders and species on both sides of the Isthmus of Panama. Some of the most widely distributed orders are, however, missing, for instance the anemone fishes *(Amphiprion)* and the wrasses *(Labroides)*. That they should have evolved after the formation of the isthmus seems unlikely. The fact that there is a mimic cleaner shows

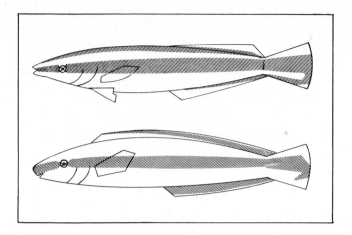

Figure 2. A cleaner (above) and its imitator (below).

that the cleaner wrasse is an old species. Its ancestral form, which was probably very similar to the present-day wrasse, could well have lived in both areas and have died out only after the forming of the isthmus in the Caribbean region, perhaps because of the cooling in the Ice Age which had a more powerful effect here than in the vast expanse of the Indo-Pacific. With it the 'ecological niche' of the cleaners would also have been opened up and we would now observe a great number of different species of fish competing for this niche. The astonishing resemblance which the most successful cleaners bear to those in the Indo-Pacific would be explained if one assumes that the original cleaners carried a very similar marking and that the hosts were attuned to this signal as receptors, as is mostly the case. The innate knowledge of the cleaners was not necessarily lost when it died out; it could have survived in the hosts. But then those fish which already bring with them certain pre-adaptations—longitudinal stripes—will take over the role of cleaner most successfully. The inborn 'taste' of the host fish will exert a selection pressure which finally brings about a far-reaching assimilation of the new cleaners to the primitive form.

In fact gobies and wrasses are so alike that even fish easily mistake the one for the other. In the aquarium Pacific host fishes do not hesitate to call up the Caribbean gobies to groom them and, vice versa, Caribbean hosts invite the Indo-Pacific wrasses to do the same.

Colour Photograph. Coral fish with cleaner. (Acanthurus leucosternon – surgeon fish – and Labroides dimidiatus – wrasse).

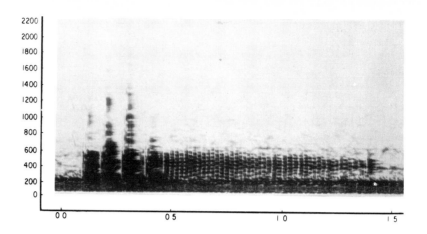

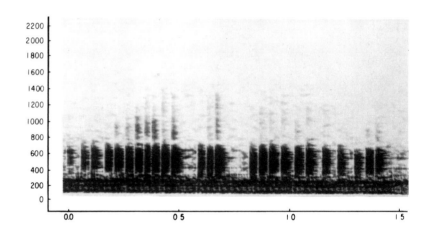

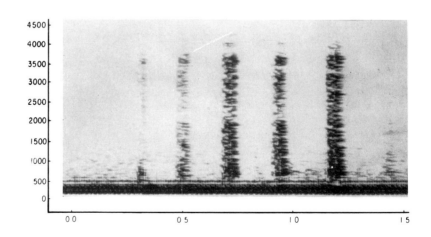

Noises under Water

Everyone knows the saying "silent as a fish". Less well known is the fact that fish are not all that silent, that they have well developed hearing and achieve understanding with one another by means of many kinds of sound. The error lay with us; we had observed badly.

The reason why the acoustic signals of fish were not heard for so long is that only a small part of sound produced under water reaches the air above–and even less reaches the ear of an observer. By far the largest part is reflected back from the surface and remains trapped in the water. If, however, we do occasionally hear some sound, then the fish in the water finds it deafening. If we want to hear something of the ordinary, everyday language of fishes we must go down into the water or use an underwater microphone. The development of echo-sounding and of 'SONAR'–a sort of underwater radar using sound waves–for navigation has, in the last few decades, given us acoustic equipment for observations of this sort, and the popularity of skin diving has contributed to the development and perfecting of underwater gear. And so the way has been opened for a new line of research: underwater bioacoustics.

The first scientists to explore this new field were overwhelmed by the number and variety of the sounds and noises that can be heard when a hydrophone is lowered from a ship–with the engine dead, of course. Describing and cataloguing these sounds and noises was the first thing which was done. Scientists like Dr. M. P. Fish and Dr. J. M. Moulton played a leading role in those years, the heroic age of underwater bioacoustics. Even today this cataloguing still goes on, but now underwater television cameras are used as well as microphones, so that it is possible to observe fish in places which are dangerous for divers and to ascertain which fish produces which sound, or what significance a particular sound has for a species.

But first let us tackle another problem. How do fishes produce underwater sounds? The sounds which are made by a fish when it swims, eats or collides with some object are of less interest to us than those which are made with special sound-producing organs in the body of the fish itself. Mammals produce sounds with the larynx. Birds have a similar organ in the fork of the windpipe, called the syrinx. We find no such structures in fish: water obviously makes other demands on the sound-producing organs. Larynx and syrinx can be described roughly as 'wind instruments'. The physical conditions for sound in air and water are, however, so completely different that the means at nature's disposal are quite unlike any type of wind instrument. All vocal organs so far found in fish are more in the nature of 'percussion instruments'. We find the most varied kinds of drums, timpani and mechanisms for producing squeaking, grunting, groaning and cracking noises. The swim bladder–originally evolved to enable fish to float at different depths–became in several species a vocal apparatus. Various forms of drum muscles are attached to the outside of the swim bladder and make it vibrate (Fig. 2). In some cases strands of connective tissue are stretched inside the swim bladder which can affect its tension and consequently its resonance. In squirrel fish the swim bladder is connected to the inner ear and in the cyprinodonts minute bones form a sound-conducting bridge between the swim bladder and the inner

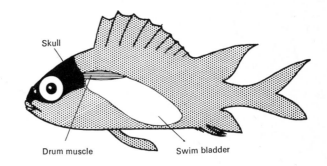

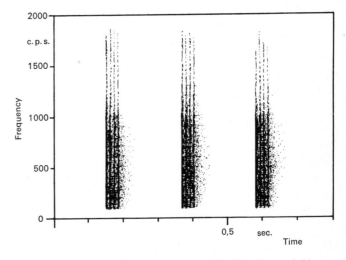

Figure 2. In the squirrel fish there are a pair of drum muscles stretched between skull and swim bladder. Nerve impulses at an interval of 0.01 sec produce a synchronous contraction of the muscle strands, which make the swim bladder produce a sound. Each of the four breaks in the sound spectrogram corresponds, therefore, to a contraction of the muscles.

Figure 1. Sound spectrograms of vocalization of three different species of cichlid fishes. Vertical axis, frequencies in cycles per second; horizontal axis, time in seconds. These sounds are observed mainly in aggressive situations while the brood is being fostered. Top, Hemichromis bimaculatus, Africa. Middle, Cichlasoma nigrofasciatum, Central America. Bottom, Pterophyllum spec., South America.

ear–the swim bladder acting as a resonator which is apparently involved in both the transmission and the reception of sound signals. Many species of fish produce cracking or moaning noises with specially modified fin parts, with their jaws, with their throat teeth or other parts of the skeleton. The sound is produced when two parts of the skeleton are pressed firmly together and then set in motion.

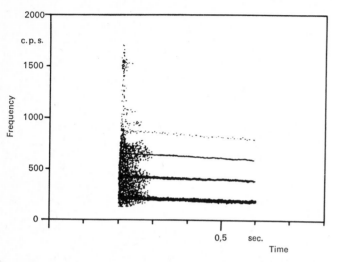

Figure 3. Sound spectrogram of the boat-whistle call of the toad fish (Opsanus tau).

Corresponding to the different sound-producing mechanisms in birds and mammals on the one hand and in fishes on the other, we also find physically different sound characteristics. In birds and mammals variations in pitch play an important role, whereas in fishes the different pitches (or spectral composition) of the sounds they make remain constant and only the rhythm is variable. In fishes, however, range of pitch and overtone content vary from species to species. The carp types already mentioned–which have little bones between the swim bladder and the inner ear–make high-frequency sounds: in many minnows the spectrum ranges from 85 to 11,000 cycles per second. In the other fish species one normally finds a very much narrower frequency range, mostly between 100 and 600 cycles per second. The well-known angel fish (see also Colour Photograph p. 41) is an exception. In spectrograms of sounds

made by this species we have found strong components even at 8800 cycles per second.

Most sounds made by fish are, perhaps, more accurately described as noises. Pure tones with pronounced ground tone and some harmonic overtones are comparatively rare. The toad fish is one exception. Its voice reminds one of a fog horn and the sound spectrogram clearly shows the harmonic structure (Fig. 3). On the other hand even a noise sounds like a tone, if it is broken up rhythmically. The groaning of the squirrel fish is a good example. The noise pulses follow one another with a frequency of about 100 cycles per second (Fig. 2). In sea brasses frequencies of about 200 cycles per second have been found. In most cases these rates are very much slower. The sound spectrograms of Fig. 1 give a good general picture. The three species of cichlids represented produce pulse sequences of about 50 cycles per second *(Hemichromis bimaculatus)*, 20 cycles per second *(Cichlasoma nigrofasciatum)* and 5 cycles per second *(Pterophyllum sp.)*.

But what is the biological significance of all these fish sounds? Fish are not mute, of that there can be no doubt: they moan, grunt, sing and croak. Do these sounds convey biologically significant information? Do they help understanding between members of the same species or are they made only to frighten or confuse predatory enemies? Several examples of the latter are known but there is much evidence to suggest that the sounds are much more frequently used as a means of communication within a species. Many fishes call only at a certain time of the year or at a particular period in their lives, and as other types of behaviour also show seasonal variations one can conclude that the sounds uttered are part of that behaviour, for example courtship. The situation is much clearer when direct observation or experiment is possible. Toad fish call more frequently if a recording of other toad fish is played back to them. Depending on their mood, squirrel fish either swim to a loudspeaker or withdraw into their hiding-places if squirrel fish sounds are played. With the Central American cichlid *Cichlasoma nigrofasciatum* (Fig. 1 and Colour Photograph) the female moans if she has eggs in her nest and a male comes too near. That is often enough to scare the male so effectively that it swims off and does not trouble her again.

Colour Photograph. A pair of South American cichlids (Cichlasoma fasciatus).

Luminous Animals

The optical techniques which animals use to communicate with one another are, usually, visible shape, colour and movement signals which they exchange in daylight. On the other hand most animals which live in the dark employ more chemical, tactile or acoustic methods and have correspondingly more highly specialized organs of smell, touch and hearing. But among the animals which live in the dark and are active at night there are some which still use optical techniques. The signals which they send out are based not on the reflection of the sunlight from specific surface structures but on the production of their own light.

The ability of organisms to produce light is generally called bioluminescence. It is very widespread, especially in creatures on the lower level of organization. The luminous bacteria, fungi, radiolaria, flagellata, sponges, polyps, corals, pyrosomes, nemertines, molluscs and many others can, however, for that very reason be of scarcely any importance for our present discussion because, so far as we know, they do not possess any sense organs capable of receiving different kinds of light signals.

It is very different with the luminous insects, crayfish, cuttlefish and fish (Fig. 1), for most of these have well developed organs capable of seeing light as well as organs producing it. Animal light production is based principally on two methods. Some luminous animals cultivate luminous bacteria in particular organs. Their light is therefore not self-generated but only 'borrowed' from symbionts. The luminescence of deep sea animals, like that of some tunicates and fishes, is of this nature. Others themselves produce in special cell complexes substances which emit light under certain conditions. Among land insects the light of the glow-worm and fire-fly, like the light of most invertebrate marine animals, is of this kind.

The phenomenon of bioluminescence was studied more closely in various organisms. The first investigator was the Frenchman Raphael Dubois. In 1887 he discovered in the luminous slime of the mollusc *Pholas* two constituents which are essential for the production of light, one of which resisted heat while the other did not. The first he called luciferin, the other luciferase. The second term shows that Dubois already regarded bioluminescence as an enzyme-like process. After Dubois, the American scientist Newton Harvey in particular made a comparative analysis of the bioluminescence of animals. In 1916 he showed that the light of the fire-fly is based on a luciferin-luciferase reaction. On a journey to Japan he found the small ostracod *Cypridina hilgendorfi* to be a particularly suitable subject for investigation. This does not itself produce light but, like the mollusc *Pholas* apparently secretes luciferin and luciferase from various glands into the water so that the water becomes luminous.

It is only in recent years that American biochemists (E. H. White, F. McCapra, G. F. Field, W. D. McElroy 1961) have succeeded in discovering the chemical structure of the luciferin of fire-flies and have been able to make it synthetically. As the fire-flies are the light-producers which are most well known and have been most studied in connection with communication techniques, it is worth illustrating the structure of their luciferin. The luciferins of other organisms look completely different.

By using the fire-fly luciferin in its pure form the American scientists were able to determine the energy balance of the light produced by these creatures. They found that every oxydized luciferin molecule has a corresponding light quantum. This means that the fire-fly light is really 'cold light' using up a maximum amount of energy.

If the self-produced light is to be used for signalling it must have features which reduce any possible danger of confusion or mistake to a minimum. That is to say, the creature's light signals should be qualitative (depending on shape and colour) and quantitative (depending on brightness, size and duration) characteristic to the species and functionally typical. Unfortunately, however, we still know almost nothing about the biological significance of the self-produced light in the majority of the luminous marine animals. The characteristic patterns of distribution, shape and colour of the luminous organs of many species of deep sea fish and cuttlefish suggest, however, that they may act as signals in various functional cycles.

There are, in fact, four possible functions:

1. The light could serve simply to illuminate the immediate surroundings: that is, the luminous organs would simply act as lanterns.
2. The luminous animals might protect and conceal themselves in their own light–by blinding attackers or frightening off light-fearing enemies with it.
3. They might attract light-loving prey.

Figure 1. A deep sea cuttlefish of the genus Calliteuthis.

4. They might emit or flash light to make themselves recognizable to some partner and thereby excite a certain type of behaviour.

We know of a number of unequivocal examples of Nos. 1, 2 and 3 among deep sea fish–one is the lantern fish *Linophryne arboriter* which carries its light organ in front of its mouth in the form of a hook to lure and capture prey.

We ought to speak of genuine signal technique only in the case of No. 4; that is, only when the light obviously is an aid to understanding between members of the same species. This can be assumed to be the case in creatures whose luminous organs are differentiated as secondary sexual features and in which the luminous behaviour occurs regularly only during the propagation cycle. These conditions are fully met in the fire-flies of the *Elateridae* and *Cantharidae* families. Best known among them are some American and Central European soft-bodied species of the *Lampyrinae* sub-family.

As long ago as 1935 the American zoologist J. B. Buck studied the so-called black fire-fly *Photinus pyralis*. The females sit in the grass in the evening while the flying males send out a short light signal every 5.7 seconds. It is only when the females answer with a signal of their own at an exact interval of 2.1 seconds, that is to say when the two partners have synchronized themselves to this rhythm, that the male lands and pairing takes place. By making suitable 'artificial' light signals Buck was able to synchronize several males and make them land.

We have a particularly good knowledge of the communications technique of the two Central European fire-flies or glow-worm species *Lampyris noctiluca* and *Phausis splendidula* from the studies H. Schwalb made in 1961. Both species occur in the same biotopes at the same time and in their abdominal organs produce light of approximately the same strength and spectral composition. The total spectral range is 500–600 nm; maximum energy output is between 550 and 580 nm, that is, in the yellow-green band.

The light which elicits a behaviour response is emitted only by the females of both species. In the evening they climb to definite lighting sites and hold the hind part of their bodies in such a way that the ventral light organs can be seen clearly from above. At the same time the males take off in search of them, flying slowly and fairly close (about 3 feet) to the ground. During flight the *Phausis* males glow continuously; but there is no proof that their light has any effect on the females. The *Lampyris* males produce no light at all. When a flying male appears above a glowing female, it folds up its wings and drops. Its aim is amazingly accurate. If females are placed in glass cylinders 1 inch wide and 6 inches tall, 65% of all flying males come down in the cylinders, the remaining 35% drop 8 inches away at the most and find their way to their partner on foot.

That the only effect of the light is to attract and guide is shown clearly both by experiments with mirrors and on females in air-tight containers. But how can the males distinguish the light of the females of their own species from those of the other species and from other, different sources of light? In the first place only relatively weak or small lights cause landings at all. If the light is more than 200 lux in the case of *Lampyris*, or even 60 lux upwards in the case of *Phausis*, the males' courting flights cease completely. Therefore it is not simply phototaxis which leads them to their goal.

Experiments using decoys show the real cause, for they allow the effective components of the signal to be tested separately. They show that the *Lampyris* males make only for lights which are very similar in brightness, size, shape and pattern to the luminous organs of their females. Only in respect of colour do they exhibit the behaviour phenomenon of what is called a supernormal releaser; that is, where the signal components are otherwise typical of the species, they prefer decoys which have a yellow light to their own females, which have a yellow-green light.

On the other hand the optical scheme which makes the *Phausis* males land is much broader. They very often 'stray' as they fly in and prefer to land by bigger, more elaborate and brighter decoys than by their own females. But they prefer blue decoy lights above all others. With them, therefore, colour is a qualitatively supernormal component. It is noteworthy that this 'mistake' in the behaviour pattern of *Phausis* is 'counter-balanced' by an uneven ration of male to female. In this species the ratio is, in fact, 5 : 1, whereas in the case of *Lampyris* it is normally 1 : 1.

It is to be hoped that the methods of communication by means of light among deep sea fishes and cuttlefish can be studied just as thoroughly as the luminous behaviour of fire-flies. It will then certainly become clear that the black depths of the world's oceans contain an unsuspected wealth of optical signals.

Colour Photograph. Luminous Brazilian click beetles (Pyrophorus spec.).

2

3

4

Turkey Signals

For reaching an understanding with their fellows, turkeys have about three dozen signals at their disposal. From all this variety we will select a few examples to show how the various senses are engaged in conveying information and how, acting as acoustic, tactile and optical stimuli separately or in certain combinations, they govern the behaviour of these birds.

Gobbling, the call of the turkey tom at breeding time, is probably the most striking signal. It can be heard within a radius of several hundred yards. It informs the hens wanting to mate where there is a tom and the other toms hear where they can find a rival. The toms have a very fine ear and answer their rivals with the identical call within a fraction of a second, then seek each other and fight for the strutting ground. How is tuning between sender and receiver achieved between toms which are a great distance apart? Learning does not seem to play any vital part, at least as far as answering is concerned. Toms raised apart from their fellows reply with the same reliability as old, experienced birds. Selectivity is never very great anyway and it does not improve as a turkey gets older. In fact, a turkey tom reacts not only to the gobbling of another tom, but to any and every loud sound in the vicinity. Under carefully controlled experimental conditions detonations, noises, frequency-modulated and amplitude-modulated tones, and even pure sine wave tones proved to be effective stimuli. Nevertheless these are not all of equal value. If one tries to start a turkey gobbling several times in quick succession with a pure tone of constant pitch, volume and duration, this artificial stimulus rapidly loses its effectiveness. If, however, the pitch is changed to some extent, say about half an octave, the tom answers again–at least a few times–until this sound also becomes ineffective. If the pitch is altered once more, gobbling starts again. Obviously the tom was not really tired of gobbling, but its sensory apparatus became selectively accustomed to the repetition of the same stimulus. If sounds rich in harmonics or frequency-modulated tones are used instead of pure tones they remain effective over a large number of repetitions. Now the sound spectrogram of the gobbling (Fig. 1) shows that this call is made up of syllables of a frequency-modulated fundamental on which a great number of harmonics is superimposed. The gobbling itself is, therefore, a signal to which the turkey tom's perception apparatus does not become accustomed, or does so only very slowly. That this is sufficient for selective tuning between the gobbling of the sender and the perception apparatus of the receiver is evident when it is looked at statistically. If all the stimuli which, under natural conditions, have caused gobbling to continue over a fairly long time are compared, the gobbling of another turkey of the same species is found to head the list. Other types of turkey calls, the calls of other animals or other noises such as the wind or thunder form only a negligible percentage which can obviously be tolerated as permissible interference.

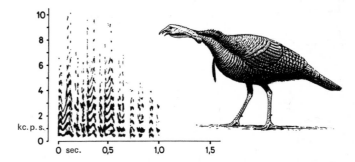

Figure 1. Gobbling turkey and sound spectrogram of the gobblingcall.

The full-grown turkey tom has hanging from his crop a bristly, black feathery beard which for a long time seemed to have no particular function and which was, therefore, thought to be mere decoration. Closer investigation showed, however, that the turkey tom uses this beard to control his position during mating. Successful copulation is impossible unless the sexual parts of both partners come into contact. In nearly all vertebrates the genitals are situated at the hind part of the body; in any case they are a very long way from the head. That produces a very difficult situation. The senses–sight, hearing, smell, taste and even, to a great extent, the sense of touch–are concentrated in the head and therefore can hardly be used for positioning the hind parts properly. The problem is solved in a round-about way. If the bodies of both partners are touching one another and their heads are close together, the hind parts are also not very far apart. With gallinaceous birds–to which turkeys belong–the hen squats flat on the ground at the mating summons. The cock mounts her, orientates himself by her head, pecks at it or holds it firmly with his beak and completes copulation. With turkeys, however, this is not quite so easy. During courtship the tom has inflated his crop to the size of a football. This, of course, does not prevent him from mounting the hen, but his beak does not reach down

Figure 2. Two wild turkeys fighting. Sequence of movement – aiming, pecking, pressing, pulling. The pecks are aimed exclusively at the red skin.

Figure 3. Wild turkey immediately before copulation. The beard on the tom's crop touches the hen's head and secures proper orientation.

Figure 4. The same pair during copulation. The hen's head is stretched out horizontally.

to her head that easily. However, the beard on his crop does touch the hen's head and assures him that everything is in order at the front end and therefore also at the hind end (Fig. 3 and 4).

One of the most striking of the turkey tom's signals is probably the scarlet colour of the bare skin at the neck and the head. It is, however, found only in courting toms which are undisputed lords of their grounds when, with crop inflated, feathers ruffed up and tail spread, they await the favour of their hens or when they fight with others of their kind. In weak or frightened toms the skin is at best grey-pink or grey, it shrivels up, feathers cover the neck and head so that bare skin can be seen only on the face; even the loose flesh above the beak shrinks until it is merely a little wart. If a strutting turkey tom which is displaying all his red (see Colour Photograph) meets a rival they embark on a peculiar contest. First, by uttering threatening calls or by leaping into the attack and striking with his spurs, the tom tries to put his opponent to flight. If, however, the latter prepares to fight and also tries to leap to the attack and refuses to give ground, a sort of wrestling match begins. Each tom, in fact, tries to peck the other's bare red skin and then to push him away or to pull his head down against the ground (Fig. 2). The skin, which looks so tender and vulnerable and the fleshy lobe which dangles from the beak prove to be extremely tough. They stand up to this rough treatment very much better than the feathers would do. This gives us the clue to the significance of the colour signal: It draws the beak to itself; the feathers, which as a rule can be renewed only once a year, at the autumn moulting, remain undamaged. Furthermore, hens and timid, vanquished toms which show no red are spared unnecessary fights.

As long as one is dealing with the communication between mature birds the problem of tuning between sender and receiver is not all that difficult. Considered purely from the standpoint of guessing, one recognizes that the individual bird has sufficient experience and, after all, there is plenty of time to discover what the other tom intends when he sends some signal. But when one observes a hen and her newly hatched poults on their first walk together, one does wonder how it is that understanding functions so smoothly from the very first. And one asks oneself: What part of the behaviour was actually the signal? And: How does the poult understand this on the very first day of its life? And again: How does the hen understand her poults when they may be her first? In addition to sleeping, eating, drinking and cleaning the poults can, from the start, do two important social things. They follow moving objects and they respond to sounds, are attracted by them and demand an answer when they themselves say something. The young poults are not really particular about what objects they follow or with whom or what they converse. They strut round with a cardboard box on wheels just as stolidly as they do with their own mother, and they are also perfectly content with an answer from a buzzer which sounds every time they have said anything. At this stage, however, they learn very quickly what the thing which they follow looks like and how it sounds. After only a very few hours this has become so firmly imprinted on their minds that they prefer, for instance, the familiar cardboard box to their own but personally unknown mother.

And how does a turkey hen know her poults? She does not know what poults look like. When her first poults emerge from under her in all their fluffiness she mistakes them for predators and reacts quite aggressively, and it is quite common for one of them to get pecked. But the cheeping releases–innately–maternal behaviour. Within a few hours the hen learns all about the look of what is cheeping so pleasantly and even if the poults make no sound for a long time she does not peck them any more.

Colour Photograph. Courtship display of a wild turkey.

Signals and Language as a Basis
for Social Behaviour

Many animals do not live alone but join with others of their own species and form a community. Such a community can be a fairly loose unit; if it is more closely knit we often find a division of labour among the members and, therefore, social behaviour. The ultimate stage is the formation of a state. The condition necessary to produce social behaviour and to create a state is mutual understanding between individual members, either by means of signals or a highly developed language. Not every animal gathering is social. *One* criterion for a social animal community is the existence of a language which makes mutual understanding possible. If this exists the members can impart information to one another and give orders for the execution of certain tasks. One simple example will show that not every assembly of animals becomes a social unit. Thousands and thousands of lower animals congregate on some coasts. They form colonies, but are still far from consituting social units. A plentiful supply of food enables them to live in the closest proximity to one another; nevertheless they remain silent, and do not speak or enter into any social relationship with each other.

Animal families and animal hordes are distinct social communities. Many apes live for years under the protection of their parents and this breeds a strong sense of kinship. The old, experienced animals lead the young and inexperienced ones, who obey them. Many birds form sleeping communities at night–for example, carrion crows and starlings–but they go their own way during the day. In these cases we find the first signs of social behaviour. If some danger threatens a starling, its shrill cry alarms the whole company, thus becoming the signal for the entire community. It is employed as a method of driving starlings out of vineyards. A tape-recording of a bird's cry of fear is played, whereupon the whole flock quickly flies away. A similar alarm signal is given by fish which form schools as do minnows. If one of them is injured by a predator, its damaged skin secretes a substance which even highly diluted warns the other fish to keep away from the dangerous area for some time.

Social relationships and the means of understanding are much more advanced among birds which form colonies. Penguins are an example. During the breeding season they form societies which are several hundreds strong. Like many other birds, both sexes make genuine marriages. Year after year the partners go back to the same place. If one arrives late, his partner may have chosen another mate to take his place. The tardy husband is, however, recognized again when he appears and the new one must go. A special greeting ceremonial plays an important role in all this. When the birds recognize each other again they let one another know this by lifting up their beaks, lowering their rudders and waggling their heads, at the same time braying loudly. This solemn ritual is the signal which shows that they have found one another again. Breeding begins at the beginning of the antarctic summer. After some weeks the female lays one or two eggs. After this exhausting experience she quits the nest and leaves the incubation of the eggs to the male. In the sea she regains her former weight and returns a few weeks later with a supply of several pounds of fish in her crop. Now it is the male's turn to go off to the sea. This changeover takes place a number of times. Every time that one of the partners returns the greeting ceremony is re-enacted. The chicks, which hatch out some time between one and two months, according to the species, soon learn to greet their parents in the same fashion. Finally, the chicks are put together in cribs. A few of the older penguins often stand round a hundred or more young ones, rather like baby-sitters, presumably to protect them from bad weather and from the skuas, predatory gulls, which can be as much as two feet tall. Meanwhile the other penguins can go off in search of food. The parents of chicks left in the nursery always recognize their young again and feed them first. So here we see already quite clearly the principle of the division of labour which characterizes a social unit.

Some of the most highly developed societies of this sort are found among the social insects which form states. In addition to the well-known honey bees, bumble bees, wasps and ants–all hymenoptera–there are the termites which are related to cockroaches. In all these insects we find a highly developed division of labour, a wealth of signals and a caste system. This caste system can be carried to an extremely advanced stage. In the case of ants and termites, members of one caste can be very different physically from members of other castes in order that they can perform their own particular tasks with the maximum efficiency. We still know very little about the 'language' of the social insects, apart from bees (cf. p. 99). One thing, however, is well established. Their many social acts and their language are not, as with us, laboriously acquired in the course of a lifetime; they are inborn and hereditary.

Figure 1 (top). Bearded penguins (Pygoscelis antarctica). A few adult birds stand with rudders outspread round a group of chicks. The species in the two photographs belong to the medium sized penguins. They grow about 2$\frac{1}{2}$ feet tall, while the Emperor penguin grows to 4 feet and the King penguin shown in the colour photograph to 3$\frac{1}{4}$ feet.

Figure 1 (bottom). Gentoo penguins (Pygoscelis papua) at a typical nest for this species. It is a shallow, rather shapeless depression in the ground with a few large stones dotted round it.

This may appear to be an advantage or a disadvantage, depending on one's point of view. Because of our ability to learn and to adapt ourselves it is possible for us to act rationally in new and unexpected situations. In any case it is for us to make use of this ability or not. While this freedom may lead us into committing lots of errors, the rigid, inborn behaviour pattern in creatures which act from instinct is a sound and infallible guide to the action which they need to take to deal with most situations.

Colour Photograph. King Penguins (Aptenodytes patagonica) swimming.

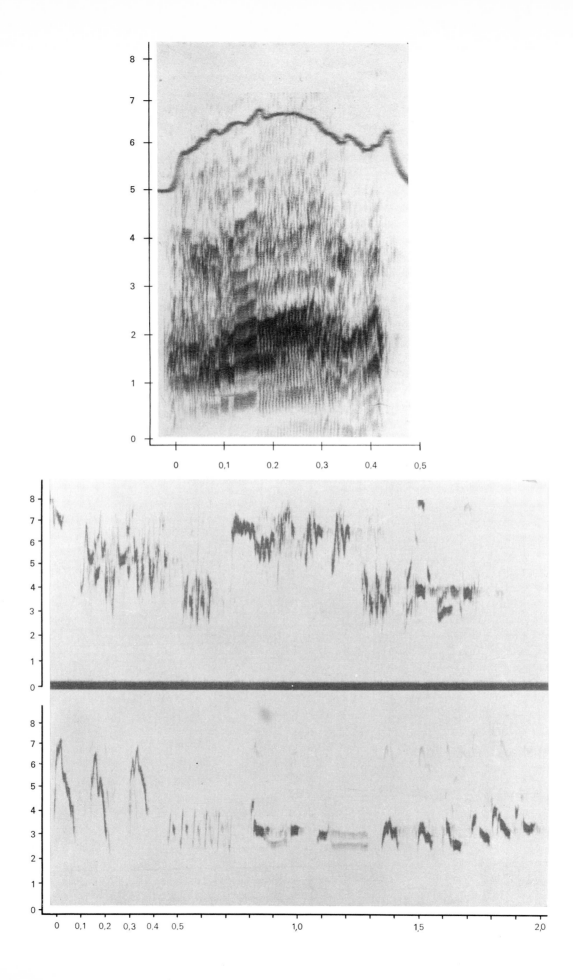

Acoustic Demarcation of Territory

Of all the means used by animals to communicate information the one known longest to man is undoubtedly the voice of birds. Even the reproduction of bird sounds by their imitation in human words can be traced back to the beginnings of history. The old names of many birds are very similar to the sounds which they utter–for example the eagle-owl, Latin bubo, and peewit.

The translation of birds' voices into human language is imperfect in two respects. Firstly, only those properties of an acoustic signal which are perceived by the human ear and, secondly, only those which can be rendered by the human vocal organs are reproduced in speech. Further distortions creep in when animal sounds are set down in the form of writing or musical notation. Bioacoustical research has, therefore, profited immensely in recent years from technical advances. In the first place by the use of excellent recording apparatus and also by the use of devices for the visual depiction and analysis of the voices recorded, thus making it possible to give a true description of them. The sonograms, or sound pictures, of Figs. 1 and 2 are more informative and comprehensive than musical notation or a written form and no special instruction is needed to read them. The time runs from left to right, the pitch goes upwards. Both are similar in principle to musical notation. The loudness of the note is shown by the degree of blackness.

The recordings show that bird notes which are inaudible to man are only an unimportant part of the sounds made by birds. Even though the voices of many birds contain overtones in the ultrasonic range, these mean no more to birds than the ultrasonic sounds of orchestral music or bell chimes mean to us. Birds hear essentially the same notes as we do and their ears are also equally sensitive, as a comparison between the threshold of hearing in man and bullfinch shows (Fig. 3). They distinguish pitch just as surely as we do. It is only in the resolution of a very rapid succession of notes that a bird's ear is superior to man's. That is why the sonogram, which can admirably capture rapid changes of tone, is superior to other methods of portraying sound.

We subdivide the sounds which birds produce into noises, calls and songs. One of the noises belonging to the first group is the clatter of the (dumb) stork, which claps its lower beak against its upper beak. The 'bleating' of the snipe is another. It is caused by the vibration of the outer tail feathers during the courting flight. An 'instrumental' sound is made by the woodpecker, which 'drums' on a dry branch.

On the other hand *calls* and *songs* are produced with the vocal organs. The syrinx, which is peculiar to birds and is located where the windpipe divides into the two bronchial tubes, plays the major role. The syrinx of song birds is equipped with eight pairs of muscles whose control is mediated by a special arrangement of innervation. The larynx, the most important organ for vocalization in mammals, is of less importance.

The *calls* provide a great variety of means to 'understanding' or 'conveying a mood'. Depending on the information which they contain or on their social function, they are described as attracting calls, mood sounds, begging calls, warning cries, cries of fear, threatening sounds etc. Although the calls of the species are more varied than the colours of their plumage, certain general rules connected with their purpose can be recognized in their acoustical structure. Attracting calls differ, for example, from species to species. Even the layman can distinguish between the bullfinch's melodious, flute-like note and the finch's bright 'pink'. As a rule the attracting calls consist of one or several sharply accentuated syllables; in that respect the bullfinch's call is an exception. The short attracting call might be especially good for locating the invisible caller in the bushes. Warning cries, of which Fig. 1 depicts one of the best known, namely the jay's hoarse croak, are less characteristic. The starling's cry of alarm sounds like the jay's call and has the same effect, even on alien bird species. The warning cries of many small birds have this in common–they make the location of the long-drawn-out sound difficult, so that the bird raising the alarm helps its neighbour without endangering itself. The great similarity between the warning calls of reed bunting, blackbird, coal-tit, blue tit and bullfinch facilitates understanding between species about a common enemy. As a general rule it is true to say that birds do not need to learn the meaning of their calls. When young birds reared in isolation in sound-proof cages from the time they are hatched reach a certain age, they produce these sounds correctly in the appropriate situations in life and also answer them in accordance with their function. This comprehension is inherited. Here is a fundamental difference from human speech, which is passed on by tradition alone and must be learned anew by every child. A condition also fixed by heredity is that every bird species commands a few dozen calls at the most. Bird song comes within the

Figure 1. Sound spectrogram of the jay's hoarse warning cry. The cry embraces a broad range of frequencies, but there is no clear tone formation. Vertical axis, frequencies in kilocycles; horizontal axis, time in seconds.

Figure 2. Sound spectrogram of two robin stanzas. (Units as in Fig. 1).

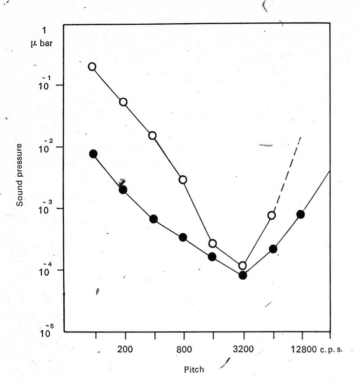

Figure 3. Threshold of hearing graph of the bullfinch (—o—) compared with that of man (—•—). The song bird's ear is equally sensitive, but only within the narrower range of its own voice.

The songs of different bird species are characteristic and give the bird-lover his most important means of identification. In addition an expert can often distinguish between individual songsters. In some cases such as in the wood wren which produces very simple stanzas, the song is equally stereotyped and seems to be genetically fixed like the calls. More frequently it seems to be made up of a combination of inherited tendency and learned motifs or whole stanzas; the songs of the bullfinch and the robin are examples. Finally, the songs of starlings and bastard nightingales consist of elements which are copied more or less exclusively from other song birds. Such birds 'mock'. In many birds which mimic in this way the 'learning' of the song is completed when it is still a nestling, months before the first 'quiet' song is uttered. The nestlings have the good fortune to hear only or almost exclusively their father's singing. Consequently, a 'family tradition' of song can be established.

Birds' songs provide ample opportunity for variations as they are composed of different notes or motifs. Many of our songsters, such as the robin (Fig. 2) or the nightingale, possess a repertoire of several stanzas. A supreme achievement came from a thrush whose recorded song ran to 193 stanzas. The ability to learn song and the possibility of combining its elements in different ways show that bird song has affinities with human speech. But the information imparted is meagre. Apart from something like "Here is a male with a territory and eager to mate", a bird's song tells other members of its species hardly anything at all.

To us bird song seems something of a useless treasure, a sort of unnecessary luxury among life's other, more practical expressions of the struggle for existence, though it has fundamental points of contact with human music. Of the elements of music—melody, harmony, rhythm, form, tempo, dynamics and sound colour—bird song lacks only harmony. Harmony is a simultaneous sounding of notes, whereas the consecutive sounding is given by the melody. The friendship which man has felt for song birds from time immemorial also springs from the seemingly pointless vocal displays which they put on, as though birds burst into song for their own joy or for ours. The functional reason for demarcating territory was, of course, already known to Aristotle and Pliny.

functional cycle of propagation and, together with other behaviour patterns, is controlled by hormones. When the sexual glands begin to mature in young males and become active again in old birds after the autumn moulting, the voice is repeatedly raised in the 'quiet' note. With interruptions due to the winter this develops by the spring into the full, 'loud' song, which is often thematically poorer. The loud song is usually produced by the male bird which is occupying a territory with a nesting place and so it is often called a 'territorial song'. This song is primarily intended to mark the extent of the territory occupied. A bird in possession of a territory sings more beautifully at the boundaries of a neighbouring rival. The song occasionally provokes a real fight, but in general its effect is preventive. It scares off intruders and possible rivals. On the other hand females ready to mate are attracted and are tolerated or greeted by the owner of the territory. If the joyous song of a male which has paired stops, the female may depart.

Colour Photograph. The warning croak of the jay (Garrulus glandarius) is well known to most bird-lovers.

Odour Signals as a Means of Demarcating Territory

When we see a bird flying we probably think of it as living a free life. If, however, we take the trouble to observe an animal in its natural environment over a longish period we soon see that this first impression was quite false. We realize that in most cases even the free living animal is tied to a definite and very circumscribed living area. There it lives alone or together with a few other known members of its own species. Strangers are usually attacked violently if they overstep the boundaries of this area. Many animal species demarcate the limits of their territory in their own special way. They do this by using signals which indicate to every alien member of the species that this is where a demarcated territory begins and that it must expect to be attacked if it does not respect the boundary.

Most of the mammals draw a fence which can be perceived only by the nose. For instance the badger (Colour Photograph) possesses a gland pocket near the base of its tail, and with a secretion from this it marks all the points which to it seem to be the most important, right up to the extreme limit of its territory. It does this by pressing its hind quarters firmly on the objects to be marked–the stones by its paths, tree trunks and even bare earth. A tame badger even greets its master by stamping on the toes of his shoes, thus distinguishing him as its personal 'possession'.

Just like badgers, martens, mongooses (Herpestes) and among the rodents for example the agoutis (Dasyprocta) also leave their mark. The males of the Indian antelope (Antilope cervicapra) have large antorbital glands which they can open or close at will. The buck marks the twigs of the bushes in its territory with the strong smelling secretion by carefully dragging the opened gland over the ends of the branches which are to be marked. In the chamois buck there are two glands situated behind the horns. They swell up at breeding time and release a secretion which the chamois spreads on plants and bushes. The brown bear puts marks near its boundary tree with the urine which it makes while rubbing itself against the trunk. It rolls in the urine from time to time in order to rub the impregnated place on the trunk again. Bisons do exactly the same. The odour marks which an animal continually applies in its haunt are rather like chemical notice boards. They are meant to inform other members of the species of what, put into human language, would be something like: "I live here. This is my property. Keep away!" At the same time, however, they also serve as orientation marks for the regular, legitimate tenant itself. House mice and brown rats, and even insects like the stingless South American bee *Trigona postica* make small odour marks along their paths and then run like trains along these tracks which can be seen as dark coloured paths.

The way these odour marks are made often seems very odd to us. The bull hippopotamus shoots its stream of urine out backwards against its short tail and at the same time releases its droppings. It then spreads the mixture widely by swishing its tail on the surrounding trees and bushes. In this way the hippopotamus creates its home atmosphere. Years ago I kept a little bush-baby *(Galago)*, a cleanly little creature with grey wooly fur, big eyes and bare, black hands and feet. It slept by day and roamed about the house by night. After some time my wife and I were amazed to discover some dark spots here and there on the wall, on various pieces of furniture in the living room and also in the bath. They were the very places on which the animal used to step as it clambered about. Soon afterwards we saw how they originated. There sat the little *Galago* shooting its urine on to the palms of its hands. When it had finished it rubbed this on the soles of its feet. Afterwards it set off on its evening climb and left its tracks everywhere. This was how it marked its path and when it climbed through the dark branches of the trees outside, it only needed to snuff along its odour trail to find its way back home. I observed a very remarkable form of odour marking in the tanrec hedgehog. This small Madagascan insect-eater spits on the place it wants to mark and at the same time wets one hand by pawing the spot. It then stretches its wet hand out behind, scratches its side several times and then, immediately, the place which is to be marked (Fig. 1). The performance is repeated many times. In this way and using its spittle as a medium, the tanrec transfers its strong body odour on to the object.

Sometimes the odour also serves to demonstrate an animals' rank and strength. Everyone probably knows the way our dogs mark particular points in their territory by lifting a leg. At many corners the males carry out regular odour duels, each one endeavouring to put his own odour mark above, and if possible much higher than that of the previous dog. Where an especially large dog has left his sign behind him, a little puppy puts its tail between its legs and runs away.

Thus the smell of a strange odour mark is intimidating. On the other hand one's own odour marks have a soothing and fortifying effect. For example, a tame badger I had raised

Figure 1. The tanrec hedgehog (Echinops telfairi) first scratches itself (top) and then rubs its own body odour on to the thing to be marked, here the head of its keeper (bottom), with its paws.

was always extremely frightened in strange surroundings. But it calmed down immediately if I held the toes of my shoes, which it had often marked, to its nose.

Perhaps that is also the reason why a male hamster which enters the area of a female at mating time in the early summer first marks the strange area by rubbing its flanks against tufts of grass and stones. Only then does it begin to court the female. And if the male finally goes into her pen it interrupts its courting to put its odour mark on the walls as well.

A number of mammals mark not only objects but also other members of their own species. Male tree porcupines *(Erethizontidae)* run erect on their hind legs towards the female and drench her in urine. Male rats behave less dramatically. They clamber over the females and moisten them with a few drops of urine. But in principle it is the same symbolic possessive act. With these sociable rodents, however, the males and the females mark one another with their odour, the high-ranking males being particularly active. This is the origin of the odour by which all members of a pack of rats recognize one another. Strange rats which are added to a pack are always severely attacked but so are members of the pack who have been removed from it for a few days. The observations of Schultze-Westrum in 1963 are of especial interest in this context. He found that short-headed flying phalangers *(Petaurus breviceps)* make marks with their frontal and sternal glands and with their urine. While they mark their living area particularly with their urine, the two glands are used primarily to mark other members of the species. The males and females of this species who live in clans rub their foreheads against the sternal region of the opposite sex. In this way there arises an odour spectrum which is specific to the clan and in which the odour marks of strong males are predominant. Thus the odour mark finally becomes the sign by which members of the clan or the pack recognize one another.

Colour Photograph. A badger (Meles meles) leaving its set.

INDEX

Bibliography - General

BUDDENBROCK, W., *The Senses*, Trs. Frank Gaynor. University of Michigan Press, Ann Arbor, 1958

BUNNING, E., *Physiological Clocks: Endogenous Diurnal Rhythms and Biological Chronometry*. Academic Press, New York, 1965

FRAENKEL, G. S., and GUNN, D. L., *The Orientation of Animals*, Dover Publications Inc., New York, 1961

FRANK, H. (editor), *Kybernetik*, Brücke zwischen den Wissenschaften. Umschau, Frankfurt/M., 1965

FRISCH, K. VON, *About Biology*, Trs. Esla B. Lowenstein. Oliver and Boyd, Edinburgh and London, 1962

FRISCH, K. VON, *Bees: Their Vision, Chemical Senses and Language*. Cornell University Press, Ithaca, New York, 1950

FRISCH, K. VON, *Biology*, Trs. Jane M. Oppenheimer. Harper and Row, New York, 1964

FRISCH, K. VON, *The Dancing Bees:* An Account of the Life and Senses of the Honey Bee, Trs. Dora Ilse. Methuen, London 1954

GALAMBOS, R., *Nerves and Muscles*. Doubleday, New York, 1962

LORENZ, K., *King Solomon's Ring*, Trs. Marjorie Kerr Wilson. Methuen, London, 1952

LORENZ, K., *On Aggression*. Methuen, London, 1966

LORENZ, K., *Über tierisches und menschliches Verhalten*, 2 Vols. R. Piper, Munich, 1965

MARLER, P. and HAMILTON, W. J., *Mechanism of Animal Behaviour*. John Wiley, New York, 1965

REMANE, A., *Das Soziale Leben der Tiere*. Rowohlth, Hamburg, 1960

TINBERGEN, N., *Curious Naturalists:* (On the Behaviour of Animals). Country Life, London, 1958

TINBERGEN, N., *Social Behaviour in Animals*. Methuen, London, 1965

Bibliography - Selected Papers

Control of Insect Orientation
BURKHARDT, D.: Lichtreceptoren im Tierreich. Naturwissenschaften *50*, 586 (1963)
BURKHARDT, D.: Sehzellen. Mikrokosmos *53*, 161 (1964)

Light-Eyes and Radiant-Heat-Eyes
BULLOCK, T. H. and F. P. J. DIECKE: Properties of an infra-red receptor. J. Physiol. *134*, 47 (1956)
BURKHARDT, D.: Sehzellen. Mikrokosmos *53*, 161 (1964)

Data Processing in Vision
BURKHARDT, D.: Lichtreceptoren im Tierreich. Naturwissenschaften *50*, 586 (1963)
HOLST, E. v. und H. MITTELSTAEDT: Das Reafferenzprinzip. Naturwissenschaften *37*, 464 (1950)
MITTELSTAEDT, H.: Die Regelungstheorie als methodisches Werkzeug der Verhaltensanalyse. Naturwissenschaften *48*, 246 (1961)
SCHÖNE, H.: Die Lageorientierung mit Statolithenorganen und Augen. Ergebn. Biol. *21*, 161 (1959)

The Ear as a Signal Receiver
BÉKÉSY, G. v.: Experiments in Hearing. McGraw – Hill, New York 1960
FELDKELLER, R. und E. ZWICKER: Das Ohr als Nachrichtenempfänger. S. Hirzel, Stuttgart 1956

Owls – Acoustic Location
KLENSCH, H.: Die Lokalisation des Schalles im Raum. Naturwissenschaften *36*, 145 (1949)
SCHWARTZKOPFF, J.: Die Stufenleiter des Hörens. Umschau *60*, 4 (1960)

Gravity Orientation under Water
HOLST, E. v.: Die Arbeitsweise des Statolithenapparates bei Fischen. Z. vgl. Physiol. *32*, 60 (1950)
HOLST, E. v. und H. MITTELSTAEDT: Das Reafferenzprinzip. Naturwissenschaften *37*, 464 (1950)
HOLST, E. v.: Die Tätigkeit des Statolithenapparates im Wirbeltierlabyrinth. Naturwissenschaften *37*, 265 (1950)
MITTELSTAEDT, H.: Probleme der Kursregelung bei freibeweglichen Tieren. In: Aufnahme und Verarbeitung von Nachrichten durch Organismen. S. Hirzel, Stuttgart 1961
SCHÖNE, H.: Über den Einfluß der Schwerkraft auf die Augenrollung und auf die Wahrnehmung der Lage im Raum. Z. vgl. Physiol. *46*, 57 (1962)

Location by the Nose
FEHRINGER, O.: Die Welt der Säugetiere. Droemer, München 1953
MONCRIEFF, R. W.: The Chemical Senses. Leonard Hill, London 1951
WRIGHT, R. H.: The Science of Smell. G. Allen and Unwin, London 1964
ZOTTERMAN, Y. (Edit.): Olfaction and Taste. Pergamon Press, Oxford, London, New York 1963

Insect Antennae
BURKHARDT, D. und G. SCHNEIDER: Die Antennen von Calliphora als Anzeiger der Fluggeschwindigkeit. Z. Naturforschg. *12b*, 139 (1957)
MARTIN, H.: Zur Nahorientierung der Biene im Duftfeld, zugleich ein Nachweis für die Osmotropotaxis bei Insekten. Z. vgl. Physiol. *48*, 481 (1964)
SCHNEIDER, D.: Vergleichende Rezeptorphysiologie am Beispiel der Riechorgane von Insekten. Jahrb. der Max-Planck-Gesellschaft 1963, 150 (1963)
STEINER, G.: Zur Duftorientierung fliegender Insekten. Naturwissenschaften *40*, 514 (1953)

The Nerve as an Electro-Chemical Conduction Path
MURALT, A. v.: Neue Ergebnisse der Nervenphysiologie. Springer, Berlin, Göttingen, Heidelberg 1958

Motor Neurons
ECCLES, J. C.: The Physiology of Synapses. Springer, Berlin, Göttingen, Heidelberg 1964

The Control Circuit in Aimed Movement
HEDIGER, H. und H. HEUSSER: Zum »Schießen« des Schützenfisches, *Toxotes jaculatrix*. Natur und Volk *91*, 237 (1961)
LÜLING, K. H.: Morphologisch-anatomische und histologische Untersuchungen am Auge des Schützenfisches *Toxotes jaculatrix* nebst Bemerkungen zum Spuckgehaben. Z. Morph. Ökol. Tiere *47*, 529 (1958) Der Regelkreis gezielter Bewegungen
MITTELSTAEDT, H.: Die Regelungstheorie als methodisches Werkzeug der Verhaltensanalyse. Naturwissenschaften *48*, 246 (1961)
MITTELSTAEDT, H.: Regelung und Steuerung bei der Orientierung der Lebewesen. In: Regelungsvorgänge in der Biologie. R. Oldenburg, München 1956

Messenger Substances in the Organism: Hormones
ALTNER, H.: Sekretionsvorgänge im Wirbeltiergehirn. Naturwissenschaften *52*, 197 (1965)
BARGMANN, W.: Das Zwischenhirn-Hypophysensystem. Springer, Berlin, Göttingen, Heidelberg 1954
EULER, U. S. and H. HELLER (Edit.): Comparative Endocrinology. Academic Press, New York, London 1963
SCHARRER, E. und B. SCHARRER: Neurosekretion. In: Handbuch der mikroskopischen Anatomie des Menschen, IV/5. Springer, Berlin, Göttingen, Heidelberg 1954

From the Third Eye to a Hormone Gland: the Pineal Body
ARIENS KAPPERS, J. and J. P. SCHADÉ (Edit.): Structure and Function of the Epiphysis Cerebri. Progress in Brain Research X. Elsevier, Amsterdam 1965
WURTMAN, R. J. and J. AXELROD: The Pineal Gland. Scientific American *213*, July 1965, 50 (1965)
MOTTE, I. DE LA: Untersuchungen zur vergleichenden Physiologie der Lichtempfindlichkeit geblendeter Fische. 2 Verlag. Physiol. *49*, 58 (1964)

How Does a Bee see Colour?
DAUMER, K.: Blumenfarben, wie sie die Bienen sehen. Z. vgl. Physiol. *41*, 49 (1958)

Flower Colours as Signals for Insects and Birds
DAUMER, K.: Blumenfarben, wie sie die Bienen sehen. Z. vgl. Physiol. *41*, 49 (1958)
KUGLER, H.: Einführung in die Blütenökologie. G. Fischer, Stuttgart 1955

Orchids and Mimicry
KULLENBERG, B.: Studies in *Ophrys* pollination. Zool. Bidrag Uppsala *34*, 1 (1961)

Echo Location at Night
GRIFFIN, D. R.: Listening in the Dark. Yale University Press, New Haven 1958
MÖHRES, F. P.: Die Fledermaus auf Tonband. Die BASF 7, 168 (1957)
SCHWARTZKOPFF, J.: Vergleichende Physiologie des Gehörs. Fortschr. Zool. *12*, 206 (1960)
SCHWARTZKOPFF, J.: Vergleichende Physiologie des Gehörs und der Lautäußerungen. Fortschr. Zool. *15*, 214 (1963)

Electric Location by Fishes
LISSMANN, H. W.: Electric location by Fishes. Scientific American *208*, March 1963, 53 (1963)

How the Salmon Migrates
HASLER, A. D.: Homing orientation in migrating fishes. Ergebn. Biol. *23*, 94 (1960)
TEICHMANN, H.: Die Chemorezeption der Fische. Ergebn. Biol. *25*, 177 (1962)
WRIGHT, R. H.: The Science of Smell. G. Allen and Unwin, London 1964

The Compass and the 'Internal Clock' of Migrant Birds
DELVINGT, W. u. J. LECLERCQ: Die Orientierung bei Zugvögeln. Endeavour 22, Nr. 85, 27 (1963)
HOFFMANN, K.: Versuche zu der im Richtungsfinden der Vögel enthaltenen Zeitschätzung. Z. Tierpsychol. *11*, 453 (1954)
KRAMER, G.: Orientierte Zugaktivität gekäfigter Singvögel. Naturwissenschaften *37*, 188 (1950)
SAUER, F.: Die Sternenorientierung nächtlich ziehender Grasmücken (*Sylvia atricapilla, borin* und *curruca*). Z. Tierpsychol. *14*, 29 (1957)

The Language of Bees
FRISCH, K. v.: Die Tänze der Bienen. Österr. Zool. Z. *1*, 1 (1946)
FRISCH, K. v.: Die Sonne als Kompaß im Leben der Bienen. Experientia (Basel) 6, 210 (1950)

What Signals will Catch a Male?
BUDDENBROCK, W. v.: Das Liebesleben der Tiere. Athenäum, Bonn 1953
LORENZ, K.: Die angeborenen Formen möglicher Erfahrung. Z. Tierpsychol. *5*, 235 (1943)

MAGNUS, D.: Experimentelle Untersuchungen zur Bionomie und Ethologie des Kaisermantels *Argonnis paphia* L. Z. Tierpsychol. *15*, 397 (1958)

TINBERGEN, N., J. D. MEEUSE, L. K. BOEREMA and W. W. VAROSSIEAU: Die Balz des Samtfalters, *Eumes semele* L. Z. Tierpsychol. *5*, 182 (1942)

Grasshopper's Songs

BUSNEL, R. G. (Edit.): Acoustic behaviour of animals. Elsevier, Amsterdam 1963

HASKELL, P. T.: Insect sounds. Witherby, London 1961

SCHWARTZKOPFF, J.: Vergleichende Physiologie des Gehörs und der Lautäußerungen. Fortschr. Zool. *15*, 214 (1962)

How is the Signal Flag Rolled Up?

PORTMANN, A.: Tarnung im Tierreich. Springer, Berlin, Göttingen, Heidelberg (1956)

Colour Signals as a Dynamic Means of Demarcating Territory

LORENZ, K.: Naturschönheit und Daseinskampf. In: Darwin hat recht gesehen. Opuscula 20. Verl. Neske, Pfullingen 1965

Friendly Signals Between Fishes

EIBL-EIBESFELDT, I.: Über Symbiosen, Parasitismus und andere besondere zwischenartliche Beziehungen tropischer Meeresfische. Z. Tierpsychol. *12*, 203 (1955)

EIBL-EIBESFELDT, I.: Der Fisch *Aspidontus taeniatus* als Nachahmer des Outzers *Labroides dimidiatus*. Z. Tierpsychol. *16*, 19 (1959)

EIBL-EIBESFELDT, I.: Im Reich der tausend Atolle. Piper, München 1964

LIMBAUGH, C.: Cleaning Symbiosis. Scientific American *208*, August 1961, 42 (1961)

WICKLER, W.: Zum Problem der Signalbildung, am Beispiel der Verhaltens-Mimikry zwischen *Aspidontus* und *Labroides* (Pisces Acanthopterygii). Z. Tierpsychol. *20*, 657 (1963)

Noises Under Water

MYRBERG, A. A. jr., E. KRAMER and P. HEINECKE: Sound production by Cichlid Fishes. Science *149*, 555 (1965)

SCHNEIDER, H.: Neuere Ergebnisse der Lautforschung bei Fischen. Naturwissenschaften *48*, 513 (1961)

TAVOLGA, W. N. (Edit.): Marine Bio-Acoustics. Pergamon Press, New York 1964

Luminous Animals

GÜNTHER, K. and K. DECKERT: Die Wunderwelt der Tiefsee. Herbig, Berlin 1950

HARVEY, E. M.: Bioluminescence. Academic Press New York 1952

NICOL, J. A. C.: Tierische Lumineszenz. Endeavour *22*, 37 (1963)

SCHWALB, H. H.: Beiträge zur Biologie der einheimischen Lampyriden *Lamporis noctiluca* GEFER. und *Phausis splendidula* LEC. und experimentelle Analyse ihres Beutefang- und Sexualverhaltens. Zool. Jahrb. Syst. *88*, 399 (1961)

Turkey Signals

SCHLEIDT, W. M.: Über die Spontaneität von Erbkoordinationen. Z. Tierpsychol. *21*, 235 (1964)

SCHLEIDT, W. M. und Margret SCHLEIDT: *Meleagris gallopavo silvestris* (Meleagridae) – Sexualverhalten

Kampfverhalten. Farbtonfilme E 486 T und E 487 T der Encyclopaedia Cinematographica, Ed. G. Wolf 1962

Signals and Language as a Basis for Social Behaviour

HEINROTH, O.: Aus dem Leben der Vögel. Verständliche Wissenschaft. Springer, Berlin, Göttingen, Heidelberg 1955

SLADEN, W. J. L.: The Adelie penguin. Nature *171*, 952 (1953)

Acoustic Demarcation of Tenitory

ARMSTRONG, E. A.: A study of bird song. Oxford University Press, London 1963

BUSNEL, R.-G. (Edit.): Acoustic behaviour of animals. Elsevier, Amsterdam 1963

THORPE, W. H.: Bird song, the biology of vocal communication and expression in birds. At the University Press, Cambridge 1961

Odour Signals as a Means of Demarcating Territory

EIBL-EIBESFELDT, I.: Über die Jugendentwicklung des Verhaltens eines männlichen Dachses (*Meles meles* L.) unter besonderer Berücksichtigung des Spieles. Z. Tierpsychol. *7*, 327 (1950)

EIBL-EIBESFELDT, I.: Eine besondere Form des Duftmarkierens beim Riesengalago, *Galago crassicaudatus*. Säugetierkundl. Mitt. *1*, 171 (1963)

EIBL-EIBELSFED, I.: Das Verhalten der Nagetiere. In: Kükenthal: Handbuch der Zoologie, Bd VIII, 1 (1958)

HEDIGER, H.: Säugetier-Territorien und ihre Markierung. Bijdragen tot de Dierkunde *28*, 172 (1949)

SCHULTZE-RESTRUM, Th.: Nachweis differenzierter Duftstoffe beim Gleitbeutler (*Petaurus breviceps papuanus*). Naturwissenschaften *51*, 226 (1964)

Acknowledgements

P. *18* Fig. 1 O. Danesch; P. *19* Fig. 2 the Author; P. *20* Fig. 3 after B. Hanström; P. *21* colour photograph by Othmar and Edeltraud Danesch; P. *22* Fig. 1 H. Tscharntke; P. *24* Figs 2 and 3 after Th. H. Bullock and F. P. J. Diecke; P. *25* colour photograph by Hertha Tscharntke

P. *26* Fig. 1 H. Altner; P. *28* Fig. 2 the Author, P. *29* colour photograph by Hans-Albert Treff and Hertha Tscharntke

P. *30* Fig. 1 prepared by and copyright of Prof. Dr. H. v. Hayek-Wien, photomicrograph reproduced by courtesy of Fa. Opt. Werke C. Reichert, Vienna; P. *31* Fig. 2 a to c the Author, 2d after W. Platzer; P. *32* Figs 3 and 4 by R. Feldkeller and E. Zwicker, Fig. 5 the Author; P. *33* colour photograph by Toni Angermayer

P. *34* Fig. 1 E. Mönsch; P. *35* Fig. 2 by J. Schwartzkopff; P. *36* Fig. 3 by R. Galambos, A. Rupert and J. Schwartzkopff; P. *37* colour photograph by Edgar Mönch

P. *38* Fig. 1 H. Tscharntke; P. *39* Figs 2 and 3 after E. v. Holst; P. *40* Fig. 4 after E. v. Holst; P. *41* colour photograph by Toni Angermayer; P. *42* Fig. 1 T. Angermayer; P. *43* Fig. 2a by A. S. Romer; Fig. 2b by D. Starck; P. *44* Fig. 3 by W. R. Adey; P. *45* colour photograph by Toni Angermayer

P. *46* Fig. 1 a to f E. Priesner; P. *47* Fig. 2 after M. Gewecke; P. *48* Fig. 3 after M. Gewecke; Fig. 4 by Angaben von G. Steiner; P. *49* colour photograph by Toni Angermayer

P. *50* Fig. 1 R. Steinbracht; P. *52* Fig. 2 after J. Z. Young; P. *53* colour photograph by Ingeborg Thomas

P. *54* Fig. 1 H. Tscharntke; P. *55* Fig. 2 the Author; P. *56* Fig. 3 after H

Rein and M. Schneider; P. *57* colour photograph by Hertha Tscharntke; P. *58* Fig. 1 by Rilling H. Mittelstaedt, Roeder; P. *60* Fig. 2 by H. Mittelstaedt; P. *61* colour photograph by Toni Angermayer

P. *62* Figs 2 and 3 the Author; P. *63* Fig. 1 by A. S. Romer; P. *64* Fig. 4 the Author; P. *65* colour photograph by Dietrich Burkhardt

P. *66* Fig. 2 A. Oksche; P. *67* Fig. 1 after R. J. Wurtman and J. Axelrod; P. *68* Fig. 3 by I. de la Motte; P. *69* colour photograph by Toni Angermayer

P. *70–1* Figs 1 to 4 the Author; P. *73* colour photograph by K. Daumer; P. *74* Fig. 1 a to c W. Schacht, 1d M. Altner; P. *76* Fig. 2 after R. Granit and G. Wald; P. *77* colour photograph by Edgar Mönch

P. *78* Fig. 1 O. and E. Danesch; P. *80* Fig. 2a by B. Kullenberg, 2b by E. Coleman; P. *81* colour photograph by Othmar and Edeltraud Denesch

P. *82* Fig. 1 E. Kulzer; P. *83* Fig. 2 after F. P. Möhres; P. *84* Fig. 3 after D. R. Griffin; P. *85* colour photograph by Edgar Mönch

P. *86* Fig. 2 W. Foersch; P. *87* Fig. 1 by W. Harder; P. *81–8* Figs 3 to 5 after W. Lissman, Fig. 6 by Th. H. Bullock and S. Chichibu; P. *89* colour photograph by Douglas Faulkner

P. *91* Fig. 1a by H. Teichmann, 1b after K. v. Frisch; P. *90* Fig. 2 the Author; P. *92* Fig. 3 by A. D. Hasler; P. *93* colour photograph by Ronald Thompson

P. *94* Fig. 1 F. Siedel; P. *95* Fig. 2 the Author; P. *96* Fig. 3 the Author; P. *97* colour photograph by Toni Angermayer

P. *98* Fig. 1 the Author; P. *99* Fig. 2 after K. v. Frisch; P. *100* Figs 3

and 4 after K. v. Frisch; P. *101* colour phtograph by Maximillian Renner

P. *102* Fig. 1 the Author; P. *103* Fig. 2 after D. Magnus; P. *104* Figs 3 and 4 after D. Magnus; P. *105* colour photograph by Maximillian Renner

P. *106* Fig. 1 the Author; P. *108* Fig. 2 drawn from an oscillogram by A. Faber; P. *109* colour photograph by Maximillian Renner

P. *110* Fig. 1 I. Eibel-Eibesfeldt; P. *111* Figs 2 and 3.D. Burkhardt

P. *113* colour photograph by Dietrich Burkhardt

P. *114* Figs 1 to 6 H. Kacher; P. *117* colour photograph by Toni Angermayer

P. *118* Figs 1a and b the Author; P. *120* Fig. 2 the Author; P. *121* colour photograph by Hermann Kacher

P. *122* Fig. 1 the Author; P. *123* Fig. 2 after H. E. Winn and J. A. Marshall; P. *124* Fig. 3 after W. N. Tavolga; P. *125* colour photograph by Toni Angermayer

P. *126* Fig. 1 P. David; P. *129* colour photograph by Bernhard Hassenstein

P. *130–1* Figs 1 to 4 the Author; P. *133* colour photograph by Toni Angermayer

P. *134* Fig. 1 A. Saunders; P. *137* colour photograph by Toni Angermayer

P. *138* Fig. 1 R.-G. Busnel and J. Giban; Fig. 2 R.-G. Busnel and J.-C. Bremond; P. *140* Fig. 3 the Author; P. *141* colour photograph by Toni Angermayer

P. *142* Fig. 1 the Author; P. *145* colour photograph by Otto Färber